kep

Crosscurrents in Psychiatry & Psychoanalysis

BEING THE PAPERS AND DISCUSSIONS PRESENTED ON THE
OCCASION OF THE SEVENTY-FIFTH ANNIVERSARY OF THE
SHEPPARD AND ENOCH PRATT HOSPITAL, TOWSON, MARYLAND

Crosscurrents in Psychiatry & Psychoanalysis

Edited by

ROBERT W. GIBSON, MD

MEDICAL DIRECTOR, THE SHEPPARD AND ENOCH PRATT HOSPITAL

J. B. LIPPINCOTT COMPANY

Philadelphia & Toronto

AN EDITOR'S ACKNOWLEDGMENT

It is pleasant, reversing a usual procedure, to observe that I have never worked with an Editor and with Authors more hardworking, prompt, and helpful than those of *Crosscurrents in Psychiatry & Psychoanalysis*. The manuscripts arrived after New Year's Day, a very few much later; the bound and jacketed book will be published, easily, in April.

Carter Harrison
J. B. LIPPINCOTT COMPANY

Distributed in Great Britain by
Pitman Medical Publishing Company, Limited, London

Library of Congress Catalog Card No. 67-19659
PRINTED IN THE UNITED STATES OF AMERICA
SP-B

Foreword

A QUAKER MERCHANT OF BALTIMORE, Moses Sheppard observed
that the mentally ill were ill-treated, often confined in the family
attic or, if public charges, placed in jails and almshouses. He came
to feel that "by an increased expenditure of means for more expensive accommodations and attendants, many persons who had been
placed in institutions might have been cured, but who, from being
isolated and confined within narrow limits had become hopelessly
insane." To make such treatment possible, he left his fortune for
the establishment of an experimental institution "to carry forward
and improve the ameliorated system of treatment of the insane,
irrespective of expense."

The Sheppard Asylum was chartered by the Maryland Legislature in 1853. To it, at his death in 1857, Moses Sheppard left
$571,440, specifying that the capital must not be touched. Over
the next 33 years, the income from this bequest was used to build
the A and B Buildings of the Hospital.

Under its first Medical Superintendent, Dr. Edward N. Brush,
the Hospital was opened to patients on 25 November, 1891. Enoch
Pratt's bequest of $1,171,000 in 1896 was a major addition to its
endowment, and the Sheppard Asylum became The Sheppard and
Enoch Pratt Hospital.

The income from these two endowments, with many additional
bequests and contributions, has been used to expand and improve
the original buildings. In 1929, the Reception Building, recently
renamed the Chapman Building, in honor of Dr. Ross McC.
Chapman, the second Medical Director, was built to house some
90 patients. To a great extent, this building was designed by
Harry Stack Sullivan, and it was there that he did his pioneer work
with schizophrenic patients. The endowment income has been
used to support, in addition to the plant, active teaching programs
for resident psychiatrists, student nurses, and occupational thera-

5

pists. Sheppard has treated more than 17,000 patients, approximately one-third of them at less than costs because of the support of endowment funds.

To mark Sheppard Pratt's seventy-fifty year of service to patients, we called on members of the Sheppard Pratt Staff, past and present, to present formal papers, and a distinguished group of psychiatrists, many of them from Sheppard, as discussants. This volume is a collection of these papers and discussions presented at a two-day scientific program.

Because each speaker was free to choose his subject, the chapters cover a wide range. Yet they share common features: all of them reflect a maturity of viewpoint gained through years of clinical experience, research, and scholarly pursuits, and all of them provide a continuity of past with present. Each author chose a significant issue, seeking solutions of present problems—the crosscurrents in psychiatry and psychoanalysis.

At this seventy-fifty anniversary, we look back to the rich tradition of Sheppard and forward to a variety of new programs designed to benefit both hospital and community. The professional staff is being strengthened in all departments. A broad spectrum of community activities is being initiated. Inpatient and outpatient services are being increased in size and scope. The training programs are being enlarged. Planning is underway for major renovations that will bring the hospital plant to the most modern standards.

In all such undertakings, we have been and are grateful for the enthusiastic support of the Trustees: Bliss Forbush, LL D, President, Hon. John A. Luetkemeyer, Vice President, John T. King, MD, John E. Motz, W. Berkeley Mann, Norris W. Matthews, Hon. Reuben Oppenheimer, Frederic F. Hintze, Secretary, and Harry M. Murdock, MD, Consultant.

ROBERT W. GIBSON, MD
Medical Director

Towson, Maryland
15 February, 1967

Preface

On Being Kind to Patients

HARRY M. MURDOCK, MD

Medical Director, Sheppard and Enoch Pratt Hospital, 1949–1963

DR. GIBSON:

During its three-quarters of a century, Sheppard has had only four Medical Directors, each of the first three having led the hospital and its programs for roughly a quarter of a century. Under Dr. Edward N. Brush, the hospital opened its doors, and he guided it in its early development. Under Dr. Ross Chapman, it strengthened its staff and brought the concepts of psychoanalysis and dynamic psychiatry into a hospital setting. Under Dr. Harry Murdock, who joined the staff in 1930 and became medical director in 1949, it went through those years of ferment following World War II, when psychiatry underwent an explosive expansion in this country and came of age as a major division of medicine. It is a great privilege to me to be able to call on Dr. Murdock to open this program.

I HAVE RATHER CURIOUS feelings here today, because I have attended a fiftieth anniversary of Sheppard, and a sixtieth and a hundredth and a hundred and tenth! A Seventy-Fifth Anniversary, a diamond anniversary, is something that doesn't happen every day, and the inference is that it is rather old-fashioned and folksy and even sentimental. But I shall forego formal anecdotes, or names, or stories, and mention something that happened to me, not long ago, that has concerned me.

One of our confreres who was here in the 1930's was asked what training was like at Sheppard in those days. He replied: "In those days, we didn't know the things about treatment that we do now,

7

so we concentrated on being kind to patients, and we became very good at it." This statement troubled me, particularly because the man who made it was a very subtle and complicated kind of fellow. I was surprised that anything so oversimplified might come from him. But as I kept thinking about it, I began remembering that psychiatry has been discovered, rediscovered, and invented time after time. My own personal observation of its invention begins during World War I, when psychiatrists, assigned to Divisions in France, operated close to the front lines. Psychiatry was discovered all over again in the early 1920's, with the emergence of the mental hygiene movement and community psychiatry, and in the late 1920's, of the team concept.

I started my training in a community mental health center, the Colorado Psychopathic Hospital, and its structural design and operating premises were precisely the same as those of the projected community mental health centers now. We must remember that Colorado Psychopathic and Boston Psychopathic (now the Massachusetts Mental Health Center), the New York Psychiatric Institute, the Payne Whitney, the Institute of the Pennsylvania Hospital, and others, were all designed and opened, many in the late 'twenties, as small community mental health centers to displace the noxious great state hospital.

There was another great surge in the 1930's, when psychiatry became "popularized" and the subject of a great many jokes, and when insulin and metrazol and ECT—the beginnings of physical-chemical treatment in its modern sense—all came into common use.

Most of us can remember the rediscovery of psychiatry in World War II. Then the idea of rehabilitating acute panic states as close to the scene of their occurrence as possible, and of promptly reintegrating men into their own units was presented as if these were new ideas, although they had been in common use by divisional psychiatrists in World War I. Then came Korea, and the shift in thinking after Korea with the emergence of the concept of the therapeutic community and the therapeutic milieu. In the 1950's, too, we had the beginnings of another sort of psychopharmacology, and we had Existential Psychiatry, and Transactional Psychiatry, and Social Psychiatry and the Systems theory—all of which brings us into the 1960's. Then, in 1963, the Community Mental Health Act—which is now stimulating the construction and staffing of community mental health centers all over the country—started the ball rolling again.

For all I know, another kind of psychiatry is emerging in Vietnam right now. When I remember these things, each thought of as new and different (some of them *were*), I have begun to suspect that our associate who talked about kindness may have had a point. One thing about his statement, however, I do question. I think it is fair to wonder whether we really know as much about the treatment of psychopathology as we like to think we do. If perhaps our knowledge is not complete, a treatment program that includes simple kindness may be not entirely inappropriate today. After all, we have always thought we knew something about psychopathology. In the 1920's Sullivan thought so. A good many people still think he had something to say that was worth listening to. So did Hill. So did Edith Weigert. So did Joe Chassell. So did a good many other people who were here at Sheppard, and who demonstrated that there was something to do to help patients in their practical application of their thinking in their work with patients. They demonstrated to the rest of us that work with patients could be an intelligent thing. And during the 1930's and 1940's and 1950's, Sheppard had at least heard about Freud, and about Jung, and Ferenczi, and Abraham, and Fenichel, and Alexander, and quite a lot of people. Sheppard, too, did have some part in founding and in assisting in the growth of the Baltimore and Washington Psychoanalytic Societies and Institutes. So that it was not only a good place for patients, but it was a good place for young physicians, one where they had opportunities to see at first hand what sick people were like, and to study what was going on in them, and to develop their own ways—hopefully informed, but their own ways, not stereotyped but individual—of doing something about people's problems.

Dr. Chapman's pride and satisfaction was always in his associates. As those of you who knew him will remember, Dr. Chapman never had a "staff." I never heard him use the term "My staff"; it was always "My associates." But he had a great pride and satisfaction in his associates who began their professional careers here, and in their ongoing development. Now we see some of the results of that development today in this program, and in the influence of Sheppard's alumni in the world of psychiatry during the 75 years of Sheppard's life.

Sheppard and Enoch Pratt Hospital 1966

Moses Sheppard's Interest in Mental Illness

BLISS FORBUSH, LL D

*President, Board of Trustees, The Sheppard and Enoch Pratt Hospital,
Towson, Maryland, Headmaster Emeritus, The Friends School, Baltimore*

*For Moses Sheppard, the establishment of the Sheppard Asylum
was the climax of his service to others. His deep interest in the
humane treatment of the insane was stimulated by his knowledge
of The Retreat, founded by William Tuke in York, England,
and the Friend's Asylum, founded by Quakers in Frankford,
Pennsylvania. He was well acquainted also with Dorothea Lynde
Dix, the dedicated social reformer, and secured the charter for
his Asylum a year after her last visit to Maryland. This concern
of Moses Sheppard's for the less fortunate the Trustees strive to
preserve in the immediate care of patients, the improvement of
treatment techniques, training leaders in psychiatry, and developing better understanding of mental illness.*

AN UNSOLVED PROBLEM in education is how to motivate the capable boy to produce at the rate of his ability. A fascinating bit of
historical research is discovering the motivation of a Lord Baltimore, an Aaron Burr, a Sam Houston or a Robert Kennedy. What
was it that stimulated Moses Sheppard to leave his fortune, large
for its day, to found one of the earliest private asylums for the
mentally ill in the United States?

It is said that Sheppard received "his first impulse in the direction"[1] of founding a mental institution from Dr. Robert S.
Steuart, Medical Director of the Maryland Hospital, which became in 1838 the first state mental hospital *; and that this impulse
was encouraged by the activities of Miss Dorothea L. Dix, who in
1851-1852 appealed to the Maryland State Legislature to establish

* The first state mental hospital in Maryland. The first mental hospital in
the US was in Williamsburg, Virginia.

11

a mental hospital. But Dr. Steuart did not agree with Sheppard's plan to found an asylum. Without doubt, Miss Dix, a truly dedicated social reformer, with great enthusiasm for the cause she advocated, did influence him. They were well acquainted, and Sheppard secured the charter for his institution a year after Miss Dix's last visit to Maryland.

More stimulating to Moses Sheppard was his knowledge of *The Retreat,* the first institution to practice the humane treatment of the insane, founded by the Quaker William Tuke, in York, England, in 1796. A close friend and relative of Sheppard, Dr. Nathan Shoemaker, was one of the six consulting physicians of the *Friend's Asylum,* founded by Pennsylvania Quakers in Frankford and patterned after *The Retreat.* The Baltimorean visited the *Friend's Asylum* on occasion, and had in his library annual reports of both English and American asylums. These two establishments provided a place of quiet retirement, in comfortable, airy halls, facing well-kept grounds with gardens, in which the patients worked. The usual bleedings, blisterings, and purgings were omitted, and the antimaniacal medicines of the day were avoided. Chains and straight jackets were taboo, being replaced by seclusion rooms and warm baths. Sympathetic and kindly treatment with a schedule of activities assisted nature "to perform her own cures." [2] The constitution of the *Friend's Asylum* stated that it is "intended to furnish, besides the requisite medical aid, such sympathetic attention and religious oversight as may soothe agitated minds." [3]

While his final decision was in flux, Sheppard recalled an earlier experience of 1815. Appointed an Inspector of the Maryland Penitentiary, he noted the disruptive effect on the inmates of constant idleness and, at his suggestion, a workshop was established, for making felt hats. This proved a success, kept the prisoners in better physical and mental condition, and returned some funds to their families. Through the years this program, in varying fashion, has been retained. Sheppard wrote to a friend that he "had several small silent cells constructed in which I made experiments with criminals. I gained information, but it only served to convince me that there is no known scale to grade punishment. . . . to some silence and solitude is torture, to others the suffering is small, and to some it was no punishment at all." [4] "I observed", he added, "that my black brethren would lie in cells like terrapins with more than philosophical composure." The knowledge gained from watching the debilitating effect of idleness on prisoners, and the varying results obtained in the use of isolation and seclusion were factors that determined Moses Sheppard's advice to his trustees.

It is obvious that these minor factors stimulated Moses Sheppard's interest in mental illness; but the motivation of this humanitarian surely stemmed from the principles and practices of the Society of Friends, of which he was a lifelong member. From the Quakers he learned that all men are children of God and when in distress deserve the attention of those more fortunate. The establishment of the Sheppard Asylum was the climax of Sheppard's service to others.

Moses Sheppard was born a Quaker on a prosperous farm near Philadelphia in 1775. There he "enjoyed the chief comforts of the life of the period." [5] With the approach of the Revolutionary War, his parents, who embraced the Quaker testimony against all wars and rebellions, moved to Nova Scotia; on returning to the United States, they found their estate confiscated by the Revolutionary authorities. The family moved to Harford County, Maryland, where a relative gave them a log cabin situated on a small plot of ground. Sheppard's first recollection of this cabin was of "playing on the dirt floor." [6] Of six children, Moses was the youngest; and, because of privation at home, went to work at an early age in a nearby mill owned by a cousin. He had little formal education, and at the age of 19 became a clerk in the provision store of another relative in Baltimore.

Baltimore, in 1793, was a "thriving, bustling, rather bumptious town," [7] on its way to becoming one of the major ports of the East. Moses shared in its growing prosperity. Within a few years, he held the major interest in the Mitchell and Sheppard Store, invested in tobacco warehouses, owned a seine factory, purchased land in and around Baltimore, became a director of a fire insurance company, manufacturing corporations, banks, and the Baltimore and Ohio Railroad.

The local Friends Meeting promoted in its members a desire to assist the helpless and the distressed. Moses Sheppard was frequently appointed to collect money from the membership to purchase necessities for the poor, or to inspect and relieve their distress. The sums were not large—for a cord of wood, a barrel of flour, payment of rent or overdue taxes. Moses Sheppard also served as Overseer of the Poor in the Second Ward of Baltimore City. In 1815, for example, he had under his supervision 121 families of 482 persons. To them he distributed 10,883 pounds of flour, 6,850 keys of herring, 205 bushels of potatoes, 53 kegs of shad, 360 pounds of beef, 120 pounds of bread, and 182 cords of wood. Out of his own pocket, he provided for an older brother and his family over several decades. He made frequent loans to aid the idealist Elisha Tyson, friend of the Negro, and at the latter's death forgave a debt of some $10,000. Many others he assisted, usually making his contributions through a third party.

The Governor of Maryland appointed Moses Sheppard chairman of a committee of three to disburse $200,000 of State money to assist freed Negroes in reaching West Africa and establishing themselves there. "Nothing seems to have challenged Moses Sheppard more than the question of Colonization, and the contacts which grew out of this work for the colonists in Africa were most rewarding both to him and to them." [8] Hundreds of existing letters tell the story of Moses Sheppard's work for those who went from Maryland to Liberia. He visited the vessels sailing from Baltimore to West Africa to see the emigrants on their way. He corresponded with the colonist, inquired after their health and their families; if they were natives of Baltimore, he passed news along to relatives. The postscripts in his letters tell of his assistance rendered over the years by sending them clothing, seeds, agricultural tools, and books.

Sheppard was an idealist, but he was also a hardheaded, practical business man; and his letters are filled with sound advice urging work, work, and more work, by the colonists. Sometimes he seemed a bit stern: "I am dissatisfied with the whole tone of your letter," he wrote one colored woman; "nothing in it indicates industry and usefulness. . . . I must assure you, I will not work in America for a lazy Negro lady in Africa." [9] To another, he sent word, "No doubt there will be privations and sufferings and hardships . . . but these ought not to discourage you, for these are the price that all, white and black, in Africa and in America, at some time, in some way, pay for freedom and independence." [10] Concerning an emigrant who was addicted to the use of whiskey, Sheppard said, "He is a free man, and he has a right to get drunk . . . if it seems proper to him; and I am also free, and have a right to withhold from him my aid." [11]

One of the most delightful episodes in the life of Moses Sheppard was his relationship with Samuel F. McGill. In 1834, Sheppard received from Liberia a letter from a young man wishing to come to the United States to study medicine. Moses pointed out the difficulty of such a course, describing what might take place in a Southern city like Baltimore. He added that if Samuel had the courage to undertake the project, the Baltimorean with the help of others would cover the cost. "You were too young when you left the United States," he told the young man, "to have a recollection of the distinction between black and white. . . . you must not expect to hear the term Mister McGill from a white man. In the college you must appear as a servant." [12] He added, "To acquire a medical education will require unremitted application and toil."

Sheppard secured the backing of prominent doctors, lawyers, ministers, and judges for the plan, and secured permission of the faculty of the *Washington* (Medical) *College,* then located on the site of the present *Church Home and Hospital,* for Samuel F. McGill to enter as a student. When McGill arrived, however, the student body went on strike, declaring that "any person who professes any degree of self-esteem cannot conceive that the faculty would consent that students of fair complexion should mingle with those of dark skin." [13] But Sheppard refused to let the plan drop, and, after much negotiation, secured entrance for the young Liberian to Dartmouth College, founded originally as a missionary college for Indian youth. Samuel McGill made excellent progress, and was aided by Moses Sheppard through the gift of books and surgical instruments.

Thanks to his Baltimore benefactor, Samuel McGill was graduated with an MD and honors from Dartmouth College. He returned to Maryland in Liberia as the physician of the colony, and eventually became acting Governor. To the end of Sheppard's life, the two men corresponded, and their interest in one another continued. The shelves in McGill's home were filled with books sent out from Baltimore, and the local Lyceum in Liberia had its cases filled with books sent by Sheppard. In turn, the house on Pratt Street became a museum of African articles—a leopard's skin, spears, a chief's wooden headrest, a monkey skin, and carved ivory.

To mental illness, Moses Sheppard paid little attention before 1850, when he was seventy-five. Although he continued to send young people to boarding schools, he was no longer in as likely a position to meet young people needing an education. In 1850, he resigned from the Indian Affairs Committee, the work with the Seneca Indians having been successfully completed as far as saving their lands was concerned. His interest in African colonization never lagged, but the bitter contest between the North and the South over slavery had already caused many Quakers to withdraw from public effort, fearing that in settling the issue the battlefield would be substituted for the pulpit and lecture platform.

A close friend wrote that Sheppard contemplated leaving his fortune to establish schools in Liberia, but since Maryland in Liberia was about to be incorporated into the larger Republic of Liberia, the Baltimorean evidently felt public education in West Africa was now a matter for the State and not a problem for private individuals. John H. B. Latrobe, a prominent Baltimorean and counsel for Sheppard, urged his client to endow a Mercantile Library for the use and education of young clerks or mechanics; and when this idea did not catch fire, he suggested a series of endowed lectureships in the local University, or a Sheppard Professorship.

But Sheppard desired his fortune to be used to alleviate suffering; and as he surveyed opportunities, it seemed that an asylum for those afflicted with mental illness would contribute to the greatest need. In 1853, he secured a charter for an institution, to be modeled after the *Friend's Asylum* and *The Retreat,* to carry forward and improve the ameliorated system of treatment of the insane, irrespective of expense . . . first for the poor of the Society, secondly for such of the Society who could pay, and then for the poor indiscriminately." [14] He added: "Let all be done for use, nothing for ornament . . . fireproof as far as practical . . . let all the cells for patients be above ground . . . and let each patient have an attendant, if desirable." Sheppard also requested that the institution should not bear his name, a request denied by his lawyer in order to secure a charter.

He also directed the Trustees to use only the interest of his money and so to retain the principal intact. When the Sheppard Asylum opened for the reception of patients in 1891, the Trustees had in their possession some 320 acres of ground with roadways and landscaping, two major buildings (then called the Western and Eastern Divisions), the power plant, a water supply, and the original bequest in money. Thus today we are celebrating the seventy-fifth anniversary rather than the one hundred and thirteenth year since the charter was granted.

The activities of Moses Sheppard's 83 years bespeak his constant concern for his less fortunate neighbors. His concern for the individual the Trustees hope will live on in Sheppard and Enoch Pratt

Hospital, in its immediate care of patients, in constantly improving treatment techniques, in training leaders in psychiatry, and in developing a better understanding of the problems of mental illness.

REFERENCES

1. Thomas, L. M., 2nd: Moses Sheppard, 1775-1857, Humanitarian, unpublished manuscript, 1941, p. 72.

2. Tuke, S.: Description of the Retreat, An Institution Near York, Philadelphia, 1814, pp. 71-83.

3. ———: Account of the Rise and Progress of the Asylum . . . Near Philadelphia, Philadelphia, 1814, pp. 6-7.

4. Moses Sheppard to Samuel F. McGill: November 20, 1842, Friends Historical Library, Swarthmore College.

5. Thomas: *Op. cit.,* p. 6.

6. Baltimore American: February 2, 1857.

7. One Hundred and Fiftieth Anniversary, 1730-1880: Baltimore, The Baltimore Sun Supplement, January 10, 1880.

8. Thomas: *Op. cit.,* p. 50.

9. Moses Sheppard to Susan Hyman: June 10, 1833, Friends Historical Library, Swarthmore College.

10. Moses Sheppard to Ann Polk: June 2, 1834, Friends Historical Library, Swarthmore College.

11. Moses Sheppard to Henry Hyman: May 30, 1834, Friends Historical Library, Swarthmore College.

12. Moses Sheppard to Samuel F. McGill: January 12, 1836, Friends Historical Library, Swarthmore College.

13. Students to Faculty of Washington College: December 13, 1836, Friends Historical Library, Swarthmore College.

14. Moses Sheppard to the Trustees of the Sheppard Asylum: January 16, 1855, September 22, 1856, Trustees Room, Moses Sheppard and Enoch Pratt Hospital.

Discussion

ROBERT A. CLARK, MD

Friends Hospital, Philadelphia

I AM HAPPY TODAY to extend to Sheppard and Enoch Pratt
Hospital on its Seventy-fifth Anniversary the greetings and con-
gratulations of her elder sister, Friends Hospital in Philadelphia.
Bliss Forbush has given us a delightful portrait of Moses Sheppard.
I cannot resist adding an example of Sheppard's dry humor, also
from a letter to Dr. Nathan Shoemaker: "It has been stated in
England that more of the Society of Friends became insane, in
proportion, than of any other society or class; I don't know if it is
so or not, but there are several here and more of us half-crazy."

However many Friends may be "half-crazy" today, I admit to an
understandable pride in the contributions that Friends have made
to the care of the mentally ill. In addition to Moses Sheppard,
there have been many others. The four generations of Tukes in
England rank first: William, Henry, Samuel and Daniel. Thomas
Eddy of New York, when a governor of New York Hospital in
1818, was the prime mover in founding Bloomingdale. Thomas
Kirkbride of Philadelphia, after two years training at Friends
Hospital, became the first superintendent of the Department for
Nervous and Mental Diseases of the Pennsylvania Hospital, now
The Institute, and a founder of the American Psychiatric Associa-
tion. Pliny Earle, another founder of the APA, after four years at
Friends, became superintendent of Bloomingdale and then of the
State hospital at Northampton in his native Massachusetts. He was
a pioneer in the science of the statistics of mental disorder.

The Quaker concern for the mentally ill is still alive. Friends
joined with the Mennonites, Brethren and members of other
denominations during World War II to put their conscientious
objectors to work in mental hospitals in the United States, who
helped to relieve the cruel wartime shortage of aides and profes-

18

sional staff. The American Friends Service Committee has since arranged for many college students to work in mental hospitals. Individual Quakers are leaders and workers in mental health, for example, the present Commissioner in my own state of Pennsylvania. Friends Hospital is still expanding after 150 years of service. A community mental health clinic on its grounds, begun in only 1958, already has 400 patients on its active rolls. It recently entered into partnership with Jefferson Medical College for the psychiatric education of medical students and residents. I need hardly add that the service of Friends on the Board of Sheppard Pratt is another example of their lasting concern.

What can be said about the humanitarianism with which Moses Sheppard was so richly endowed? Three threads run through the whole length of the fabric of the history of psychiatry: the practical, the humanitarian and the scientific. A few have combined all three in one person: Philippe Pinel was the first. Friends have excelled in both the practical and the humanitarian; Daniel Hack Tuke was one of the few who was also a scientist. The humanitarians have drawn their inspiration both from religion and from the humanism of the eighteenth century enlightenment. The Old Testament tells of King Saul's melancholia being aided by David's playing on the harp—the first written instance, perhaps, of music therapy. The New Testament tells of Jesus' healing of the man afflicted by a legion of demons, and of his saying to that man: "Go home to thy friends and tell them how great things the Lord hath done for thee and had compassion on thee."

Compassion—that is the key word. A cardinal religious doctrine is that there is something of God in every man. The task of the compassionate psychiatrist, of all workers in mental health, is to fan that divine spark into a warm and constant flame. None of us believes any longer, except metaphorically, in possession by demons. Some of us find the language of religion uncongenial, and speak rather of a capacity for mature love or of a real inner self. But our problem is the same: how to seek out what is sane and strong and healthy in our patients, free it from fear, hatred and the bonds of rigidity, and help it to grow into integrated and creative maturity.

This ideal goal needs the dynamic interplay of our three methods: practical, humanitarian and scientific. Too much of one leads to extremism, hindering the progress of psychiatry. He who is only practical ends in short-sighted empiricism and eclecticism: anything that works is good. Too exclusive humanitarianism leads to sentimentality. I venture to suggest that extreme permissiveness— like the radical nonrestraint of over a century ago—leads to lack of decisive limits, leaving many patients floundering in confusion. We have all seen devotees of pure psychodynamics who refused to allow *any* patient to have electroshock treatment. Two kinds of scientific overemphasis exist: the strict organicist who can think only in terms of biochemistry and neurophysiology, on the one hand, and, on the other, the analyst (of whatever school) who never tells us the outcome of his treatment because in his voluminous writings his patients exist only as illustrations for subtle theorizing. The ideal psychiatric hospital is the one that maintains a harmonious balance between the practical, the humanitarian and the scientific, in which no one of the three is slighted or magnified in favor of another. The history of psychiatry records one or the other approach in ascendancy at different times, but sooner or later the balance is restored and the others get their proper turn. An institution as aged as the one we celebrate today has seen enthusiasms wax and wane, and now in its septuagenarian wisdom can gaze benignly on the follies of youth while going on to encourage its children to live the integrated life of sane maturity. May it serve generations yet to come!

Contents

1

Our Generation of Psychiatrists
Changes in Our Words and Changes in Our Thinking

IVES HENDRICK, MD

Director of Clinical Psychiatry, Massachusetts Mental Health Center, Clinical Professor of Psychiatry Emeritus, Harvard Medical School, Boston

The subtle transformations in the meanings of words in everyday use indicate alterations of our psychiatric understanding and practice. The denotations and connotations of commonly used technical words differ gravely, and thus confuse "several types of experience, pathology, and basic mechanisms, which should still be more clearly distinguished." Examples are schizophrenia, catatonia, hebephrenic, depression, regression, anxiety.

Words are tools of thought most effective when used and understood precisely. Younger and older psychiatrists, though using the same words, may speak languages so different that they are mutually unintelligible.

SEVENTY-FIVE YEARS AGO, Sheppard Pratt Hospital began its humane, creative, and scientific existence. Thirty-nine years ago, in September 1927, it gave me the opportunity for my second year in psychiatry. My appointment was as "Research Associate," with the privilege, which I appreciate even more now than then, of intensive clinical research with a limited number of schizophrenic patients by thorough study of their detailed histories and total personalities, followed by free association interviews* for long periods.

* Following that year at Sheppard Pratt, I undertook psychoanalytic training, so far as I knew my first exposure to free association technique. I was amazed a few years later, when reviewing my detailed records of these patients at Sheppard Pratt, to discover that I had been using consistently the free association method with them.

23

Many and nostalgic are the memories of this year, especially of the zeal and interest within this community of doctors of all ages. Dynamic psychiatry seemed to us, compared to the relative sophistication of the resident of today, a domain unexplored and untrammeled, and we shared with only a few other psychiatric centers the conviction of accomplishing something new and vital in the study and treatment of patients, something more inspiring than custodial care and more exciting than mere diagnosis.

Dr. Ross Chapman was Superintendent. His early training had been with Dr. William Alanson White (Dr. White's *Outlines of Psychiatry* should still be read today by young psychiatrists) at St. Elizabeth's Hospital in Washington, the first to apply the principles of psychoanalysis intensively to psychotic patients in a hospital. Dr. Chapman had set and tended the fires of our new interest in dynamic study here at Sheppard Pratt. My immediate chief was Dr. Harry Stack Sullivan, whose genius, or something close thereto, at its zenith in those years, was his understanding of the language of the schizophrenic; he could almost speak it himself, a language without some understanding of which none of us could understand what the schizophrenic is doing and thinking. I also greatly enjoyed frequent meetings and visits with Drs. White and Nolan Lewis at St. Elizabeth's in Washington, and with Adolf Meyer and his staff at Phipps.

Sheppard Pratt was making its generous contribution, therefore, to that new approach of the 20th century to the study of the mental problems of mankind, already known to us at that time as "dynamic psychiatry." Our objectives, new techniques and discoveries were based on the clinical study of mental contents, especially the less rational elements of the mind, with the purpose of clarifying normal and abnormal patterns of adaptation and the development of personalities.

Though these are the purposes of the dynamic psychiatry of today as well as of 40 years ago, I am not at all certain that those who practice it today approach the study and the treatment of their patients with quite the same basic premises. The purpose and the pattern of clinical work, and the manner of thinking about the data and reporting them, have not in all ways remained the same. One evidence of such changes is the implied premises and connotations of words that we commonly use professionally, especially the more technical words, modifications which are not always obvious and do not usually involve a rewriting of the definitions of their literal meanings. In this chapter, we shall use examples of words in everyday use, and examine some of the more subtle but fundamental transformations of their meaning, observing how such mutations offer keys to alterations of our psychiatric thought that are not usually identified.

I.

"Schizophrenia" is an eminent example of technical words that we use every day whose meaning and connotations have undergone more modifications than usually recognized. Such changes are not due to any deliberate intention, nor to such a systematic redefinition of nosology as Adolf Meyer once attempted, but to new ways of thinking with less focusing on definite details of the mental status. For older generations of dynamic psychiatrists (whose training was between 1920 and 1950, roughly) were in general agreement what kinds of pathology and symptomatology were thought of as "schizophrenic" and what types of schizophrenia were differentiated. This has changed; everyday cases are called "schizophrenia," which does not show those specific characteristics that formerly were considered important and definitive. Instead, "schizophrenia" is commonly used much more loosely, almost as an eponym for a variety of psychoses, usually with delusions or hallucinations, and with much less attention to distinguishing various types. Only "paranoid psychoses" and "depressions" are still differentiated clearly.

Even more vague is the diagnostic usage of subtypes of schizophrenia. The "paranoid type" of schizophrenia is no longer differentiated in most clinics from other paranoid psychoses; perhaps that is just as well, but let us recognize that it has happened. "Catatonia" is still in current usage, but what it denotes is less definite; no longer does the psychiatrist automatically test the waxy flexibility or describe the apparently complete inhibition of perceptual experience, mobility and cognition when he thinks of catatonia. Instead, almost any patient who stays by himself, mentally withdrawn, resisting communication, and preoccupied with irrational thoughts or symptoms can be referred to as "catatonic," and frequently is. Recently I spoke of a patient as "hebephrenic," and a group of residents were delighted, for, they told me, they had been perplexed for months what kind of patient was called "hebephrenic." They said that they had read of this type but had never seen one; no one of these younger psychiatrists had doubted that this patient should be diagnosed "catatonia." Such differences in vocabulary as used today are common.

Still more notable is the alteration in the daily usage of "depression." This change, too, is very general, and has developed over the years without deliberate planning. Formerly we learned to use "depression" for technical purposes in a more specific and definite sense, exactly that of the earlier word "melancholia." "Depression" then designated the domination of a patient's thought, behavior and symptoms by an *affect* of a specific and unique quality; a diagnosis of "depression" defined pathologic states whose chief symptoms and thought content were determined by this specific affect. Today "depression" (or "depressive" mood) is perhaps the commonest word in clinical use, yet it is applied to a conglomerate variety of subjective symptoms; its usage has become more indefinite, more vague than is realized. Rather than meaning a specific kind of affect, and the consequences of that affect, it has come to imply many types of mood and mental experience that are in some way unpleasant, one or another variety of *Unlust,* displeasure or dysphoria, some kind of mental pain or unhappiness. Thus it no longer differentiates depression from such other painful feelings as inferiority of self, grief or sadness, pessimism or lonesomeness, feelings of failure, or varieties of severe self-depreciation. This trend in our professional linguistics is paralleled by the constant use of "depression" by the laity, so that it is perhaps the commonest initial complaint of many neurotic patients.

The importance of such a development is not whether colloquial and clinical meanings should be always sharp and unambiguous—we don't all talk like dictionaries all day long and do not want to. But I believe that an important consequence of this particular word-mutation is a confusion of several types of experience, pathology, and basic mechanisms, which should still be more clearly distinguished, as they were until recent years. Thus cases that present classically anaclitic content and pathology are discussed as though they suffered from the same kind of affect-pathology and psychogenesis as those depressions that follow object-loss with retardation, inhibition and self-blame. This, it seems to me, is a clear example of the value of more careful differentiation of words at times; for the patient with dominant anaclitic pathology and personality type is very different in personality, in his needs and the etiology of his illness, from the classical cyclic and reactive depressions. When such cases are not clearly distinguished by words, we lack a basic element in our thinking and our study.

Strangely, the meaning of "elation" has not been similarly transformed. Even today it is not used as a grab bag for many different kinds of pleasant experience, as "depression" is for all painful moods. But words for other specific affects have become blurred. "Anxiety" is another word badly tossed about. Various states of tension are presumed to be evidences of anxiety. Patients with a modicum of bearable anxiety are referred to as "depressed," and those with noncrippling depression as having "anxiety." It is true that these two affects are often mixed and then hard to distinguish clinically; but that is insufficient reason for ignoring the difference and blurring the meaning of two elemental emotional states that primarily are as distinct as the perception of red and blue. Even the word "love" is becoming passé; a "positive relation" or "transference" is instead in fashion. But "hate" and "jealousy" may still be used.

The changes in the usages of "depression" and "anxiety" have occurred in quite recent years. A similar transformation of "hysteria" has been more gradual and taken a longer time. The neurologist's use of it to diagnose a class of symptoms that were "functional" not "organic" had been standard for generations. Meanwhile, Freud had discovered the mental mechanism of "conversion," and by the late 1940's psychiatrists were beginning to diagnose all cases of hysteria as "conversion hysteria." They had seen these cases clinically and they had heard of Freud's discovery, so now they used two words for diagnosis where one had long sufficed—and thereby eliminated the distinction between the diagnostic type of the symptoms and the clinical exploration of the conversion process that produced them.

Another classic contribution to our thinking tools had been Freud's recognition that anxieties in cases with neurotic phobias, result from the same type of genital conflicts in the same type of personalities that Freud had already shown produced hysterical symptoms. "Anxiety hysteria" and "hysterical character" then became two of the most valuable and clearly defined additions to our family of words, until, during the last decade or two, even these clearly understood terms have become vague; all are now commonly referred to as "hysterics" and the words sometimes mean little more than a "good case" for a young man.

During the postwar decades, the adoption of other psycho-analytic terms has accelerated. Again the implications of these verbal tools have been more drastically modified than generally realized. *"Regression,"* one of the most valuable transplants from psychoanalysis, is a good example. Originally it was used by Freud to describe such unconscious changes in the aims of the libido as occurred in obsessional symptom-formation; analytic data showed that unconscious fantasies derived from the genital phase of sexuality were replaced by fantasies derived from the anal. With the passing years, this meaning was appropriately extended to other processes that also involved unconscious replacements of one stage of maturity by the derivatives of an earlier one but were otherwise quite different. Thus "regression" from reality-tested thinking to autism was a useful and accurate designation: regression from object-love to narcissistic love was another, regression of the "ego" from an adult organization of the mind and personality to more childlike or infantile patterns was just as important. But, in recent years, "regression" has spread like a weed to even newer usages with less clear and well thought-out reference to processes that are not clearly indicated by the empirical data. Its current use, therefore, is often vague: when one hears it, it may mean only that the patient is worse; his psychosis has become more manifest; or he appears less neurotic, more autistic in his thinking and pleasure-sources. Much too often "regression" means only that this patient is more difficult to cope with and manage. The limits between a word generalizing superficial *observations* and a word meaning a carefully studied *process* are obliterated.

Even more striking is the constant use of such psychoanalytic words as "oedipal," "oedipal problem," "oedipal character." "Oedipus complex" is mentioned everywhere; but it no longer means a group of phantasies hidden in the patient's unconscious since infancy. With only a nose and an eye visible in the mental brambles, the little fellow's phantasy is no longer so hard to chase and catch and grab. Older psychoanalysts, remembering well the frenzied opposition for 50 years to this discovery of Freud, can scarcely believe their ears, our colleagues and students are so permissive. Eventually, however, we realize "oedipal" has almost lost the meaning it had for Freud and his earlier students, a set of deeply repressed sexual phantasies of mother and father whose empirical demonstration required long and arduous periods of expert analysis of the unconscious. Now the characteristics described as "oedipal" are reported in most every case; at least they are referred to that frequently in discussions. What is really meant is that a patient discloses some quite conscious reactions to mother and father, or to their surrogates or older people. "Oedipal" usually means little more, so far as one's clinical material has revealed, than various types of feeling, of love and hate, ambivalence and emotional attachment for the older persons in a family.

These examples of the changes in the meaning of a word all have a fairly definite, single-fact definition. The same process of subtle but important change over the years, in the direction of more diffuse, less well-denoted verbal significance, has also been affecting more abstract elements of the psychiatric language.

"Identification" is an important example of a word whose original psychoanalytic usage has been altered without intending to do so. For decades now, our standard everyday talk has included such compound words as "feminine identification," "mother identification," "homosexual identification," "phallic identification," "identification with the castrator." When one pauses to study what are the actual meanings of these compounds of "identification" when used this way, one discerns that they usually denote essentially a relatively uncomplex fact or conclusion, such as a patient's character trait, or a wish, or behavior detail, for which the single words feminine, or homosexual, or phallic, or castrating would do quite as well as the compound. This resembles the semantics of diagnosing "conversion hysteria" when one means "hysteria": a double word is used where a long-familiar one would do as well, with the implication that one has information that one does not have; and it therefore muddies rather than reveals clear understanding.

For in 1923 Freud had defined a mental *process,* which he called "identification." To understand his meaning then, we should be clear that this was the *induction of a process,* but not a direct observation, in the sense that one observes a repressed wish, a feminine trait, a mother-like act, or a phallic or homosexual fantasy. This induction of the identification process has been a major advance in understanding fundamental aspects of personality development, in understanding the psychogenesis of some symptoms, in reconstructing the origins of some organized portions of the mind, the ego and superego, in understanding vital nonintellectual components of learning and maturation. But the identification *process* is inferred from occasional clinical glimpses, like beads strung on a thread which itself is rarely visible. "Identification" used in this Freudian way is very different indeed from its constant attribution to relatively simple traits, wishes, needs, behaviors, by verbally tacking it on to simpler and more accurate words in the manner so prevalent and generally acceptable today.

II.

These are a few everyday examples of the modifications of word meaning. They represent trends which, it is worth noting, are accelerating in recent years. Moreover, let us particularly note, they are usually not changes in what the semanticists call the *"denotations"* of the words: they are not usually alterations of the primary, literal, definable meanings, but are transformations of their more usual connotations. Most of these words have not been deliberately redefined by anybody, but their accessory meanings have changed.

These examples show that recent patterns of thought are often based on less *preciseness* in our thinking than we might expect. Indeed, some recent word-usage suggests a *devolution* in this respect, not unlike the loss of inflectional modifiers as national languages age. We might well have predicted that it would be otherwise in a generation that has more and more emphasized the need for quantitation and insisted on greater exactness by the use of "scientific models," better controls and statistics, and the imitation of the more exact sciences. This aim has been attained in the adjunctive areas of psychiatry and their research fields. Yet when we return to our primary interest, the dynamic examination of the mind, feelings and subjective experiences of our patients as studied clinically, these changes in the use of our language indicate that we have actually drifted further away from precise thinking and clear differentiation in reporting clinical work than we planned or expected, or intend or even recognize. As we have commented, "schizophrenia" commonly denotes more mental states more vaguely than it formerly did; and today's usage of "depression" is even less precise. "Conversion hysteria" confuses a process induced from data and the actual observations, and so do "identification" and "regression," as used today. In these examples, diagnoses from observations and clarifying hypotheses are not distinguished linguistically.

Concurrent with less and less preciseness of our word-use has been a second trend—paradoxically, the antithesis of indefinite-ness. This is the trend to name clinical phenomena, and often to think about them, in more and more general or abstract, or quasi-abstract, terms. It reminds us that during these past 75 years (which we celebrate here), psychiatry has abandoned its sources in 19th century philosophy and in the use of philosophic theorems and terminology: major premises, subject-ego and object-ego, as-sociationism, and the like.*

As modern psychiatry emerged in the late 19th century, it focused first on more accurate description of symptoms, then on their classification and groupings for diagnosis. When the belief that all psychopathology was caused by undemonstrated brain damage receded as a universal assumption, the diagnosis of mental states led to the use of detailed observations as jumping-off points for the investigation of the individual patient's mind, its function in the adaptation of the total personality, and finally personality development. It is perhaps worth pausing to meditate on whether the recent trend to minimize fact and detail by thinking and using language more and more abstractly reveals some of the character-istics of a "linguistic regression" to our forebears in philosophy.**

This trend to think more and more in abstract words is most clearly revealed by the hothouse proliferation in recent years of the word "concept." Case material is more commonly formulated every day by ideas that are spoken of as "concepts." Teachers more often ask students their "concept" of a case. Even well-known re-search people refer to their conclusions from experiments as "con-cepts." It is so much easier and safer, especially for beginners in psychiatry, to describe a case conceptually—one can then hardly ever be in error—than it is to struggle with the uncertainties and inevitable shortcomings of a clinical summary. At clinical con-ferences and demonstrations, it is the fashion for students to make the comparison of the "concepts" or "viewpoints" of their several

---

* Possibly the gradual exclusion of "insanity" from our acceptable vocab-ulary is not due entirely to the modern intent to abolish its contemptuous image of the patient (certainly our leaders fought hard during the "mental hygiene" age (1910–1935) to advance the idea that psychosis is illness); it is due also to the wish to improve on a word like "insanity," which lumped all kinds of aberrations together.

** Freud was himself aware of this 40 years ago. He sometimes deplored, especially in informal conversation, the "new" tendencies of psychoanalysts then to renounce their former interests in content and rely on the abstrac-tions of the ego and the id, which he himself had introduced.

teachers their primary intellectual purpose when listening. But that is different from good criticism of their seniors' thoughts and discussions; it is putting a dozen conceptual carts before the clinical psychiatry horse and sitting oneself down solid in one of the carts. For the student is judging the concepts, or biases, of his teachers, rather than striving to learn to recognize and use his clinical facts. He is playing Chopsticks with the words that signal the generalized and hypothetical conclusions of the great creators of psychiatry rather than emulating their investigative labors.

Another startling example of the increased use of abstract words is the frequent reference recently to "the dynamic psychiatry concept." Often this phrase clearly has the connotation of a freedom to choose among concepts as among records selected on a jukebox: today one chooses to play dynamic psychiatry, tomorrow the "chemical concept" or the "community viewpoint," "conditioned behavior" the next, and the "social concept" or the "family concept" another day. "Dynamic psychiatry," when thus thought of as one of several alternative concepts to be switched around and on and off, is more alien than is obvious to its meaning for older generations. True, dynamic psychiatry had always accepted a few basic postulates, particularly that *subjective* phenomena may be studied with objectivity and scientific purpose, and that other sciences contribute to its total picture. But those who have made dynamic psychiatry their lifework have worked with facts in order to understand the relationship of data, not primarily with the invention of quasi-philosophical conceptual systems.* At a recent conference on the teaching of psychiatry by psychoanalysts, I was surprised that *most* of these experienced discussants, not just two or three, centered explicitly on "concept" as topics for teaching, such as what "dynamic" or "psychoanalytic" *concepts* should be taught and when.

The increasing use of the word "concept" itself is only one of many instances of the rapid increase of "conceptualization" as the primary task of psychiatric thought. "Community psychiatry" was at first a descriptive phrase, meaning the extension of psychiatry to

* Possibly the new trend was influenced in the postwar years when opponents and detractors of dynamic psychiatry found it necessary to use "dynamic psychiatry" as a slogan to attract residents and funds, though their convictions as to what was professionally sound denied its value. In more recent years, almost all publicity uses this nationally advertised guarantee of up-to-dateness, regardless of the intellectual and budgetary orientation of the particular work.

many more communities. But more and more it is thought of as a great and new idea, and referred to as a "concept" to be taught and advertised; that attitude is for me demagoguery and does slight justice to our more intelligent and honest efforts to improve our knowledge and extend our usefulness. But conceptualization of psychoanalysis is possibly the best of all these current examples of excessive use of concepts, especially when it is the major focus of a didactic discipline. There is little controversy today, as there has been for 50 years, about the importance of the unconscious. All good psychiatrists (and most of their enemies as well) now accept it, teach it in orthodox lectures, and have established it as a concept for the student before he himself has the clinical opportunity to observe its effects. The same is true of "conceptualizing" such observable facts as repression, resistance, transference, and especially the ego and ego-defenses.

This drift toward concept thinking represents a fundamental transformation in psychiatry and the thinking of psychiatrists, no matter how dynamic the purpose or correct the generalizations. The investigative psychiatrist who tends to focus on interpretation by abstraction thus draws the curtain on intensive study of the individual's content. It is not unlike the difference between a good road map to simplify one's journey and explicate one's route, and a really observant travel plan. The straight red line on the road map is strictly correct in useful ways, and the throughway is well engineered. But if the clinical investigator follows the red line in an all-or-none way, he fails to learn about the winding roads, the towns, the forks and crossroads, the hills and valleys, the foliage and homes, all of them part of this countryside, too. The psychiatrist should not ignore the importance of the red line that all ramps lead to, but he should not be compelled to think only of the generalizations and forget the ins and outs and variable details of his patient's mind and personality.

This type of cerebration is one mode of psychiatric thinking. The demand for "concepts" and "conceptualization" is far more frequent and mandatory than 20 years ago, and involves less total effort to discover and appraise the details of mental experience.

III. Conclusion

A professional language, as all other languages, displays a complex process of evolution at work constantly producing changes. Mutations of verbal units come about, often unpredictably; and so do concurrent processes of natural selection. Some words and the thought-patterns they beget are altered apparently as naturally as tissues when growing; some become obsolescent and die.

In addition to intrinsic development, however, extrinsic, environmental forces affect the selection and modification of words. Our language reacts to what we do, what we want to do, and what we think about; and to what the various groups with which we associate are thinking and saying. Occasionally, the stimulus is a new definition. More often, such direct artificial forces are more complex, such as the professional fashions of the day, what is popular, and sometimes glamorous to mouth. We are affected by the characters and demands of those who have influence, by job demands, and by the professional trading marts. A conspicuous influence since World War II has been the impact exerted by both physiologic and social sciences on what psychiatrists do, what we say and how we say it.

The prominence of the new drugs in our daily reading and work may have had a more definite effect on our professional lexicon than we ever pause to think about, contributing to some of the modifications noted here. For pharmaceutical houses and researchers in pharmacology, of course, adopt our psychiatric language. But they and we overlook the fact that symptoms and syndromes affected by a drug are often far less precisely estimated than is intended by our classification of mental states. Thus a drug is called an "antidepressant," it produces effects on a variety of conditions, and sooner or later we come to class together these various conditions affected by the drug and think of them all as "depressions." Important traditional distinctions of mental states are more precise, yet overlooked by the drug-givers; unwittingly the meaning of the word "depression" has been changed. Similarly, the phenothiazines are "antipsychotic"; and eventually various psychotic syndromes that they affect are no longer so carefully distinguished. A variety of states that are "tranquilized" by tranquilizers are more and more thought of as "anxiety," but are less clearly a direct product of the painful signal that that word is intended to denote. The new drugs have affected not only the physiology of our patients but our language and our thinking too.

Changes in words and their connotations are details of language evolution, of mutations that perhaps are native to the biology of the human brain which produces language, and to reactions to the changing word milieu in which it works. It is not my intention to attempt an artificial halting or correction of so basic a fact of semantics as the inevitable change and development of language. I do want to highlight the fact these changes are occurring. For it can help a senior psychiatrist to realize that a younger colleague, when he speaks of the patient as "depressive," may mean something quite different from what Karl Abraham or William Alanson White meant with their more precisely defined usage. And the younger psychiatrists, too, may need to appreciate this when they read the older scientific works, the progenitors of their modern psychiatry; a failure to do so may even be contributing to the tendency of many to take less interest than formerly in the historical origins of today's ideas and knowledge. At least there is little exaggeration in saying that, even though a younger generation of psychiatrists and the older psychiatrists use the same words, they sometimes speak in somewhat different languages with different premises and different unverbalized connotations. Their usages thus resemble two dialects, closely related but not mutually intelligible. Let us recognize and clarify these semantic artifacts whenever we can.

Finally, let us note, this study of word changes is relevant not only to our use of words as tools, as vocabulary. Words are also important indicators of contemporary changes in the way we think; of the emergence of new thought-patterns, which are not always quite obvious, and which include implicit assumptions that we are not conscious of. For language is the record of most of the history of the human mind, of the human individual, his complexities and his nuances, and his functioning allegiance to a clan or to a fashion of the period. It is still slow and difficult, as it is for the professional linguist, to decode this knowledge. Even so, we can scarcely doubt the principle that we can study our words and their vicissitudes in order to discover hidden facts concerning our work; it would be very like the psychiatrist's use of symptoms as starting points for the clinical exploration and understanding of complicated personality adjustments.

Discussion

Leo H. Bartemeier, MD

Medical Director, The Seton Psychiatric Institute, Baltimore

THIS SCHOLARLY AND COURAGEOUS contribution to this scientific program calls attention to one aspect of what Freud had in mind about the probable watering-down of psychoanalytic theory in this country. I am in full accord with Dr. Hendrick's observations about our present-day psychiatrists and the changes in our language and thinking. I, too, repeatedly observe how hospitalized patients who manifest delusions and hallucinations are hastily labeled schizophrenic, undifferentiated, paranoid, and rarely, if ever, hebephrenic. There is an assumption of knowledge without carefully conducted clinical investigation, without serious consideration of differential diagnosis, and without the continuing utilization of clinical observation, which has seemingly become a lost art in our medical armamentarium.

The technical term "insight" is currently used to signify understanding or lack of understanding of oneself, instead of what I knew as its original psychoanalytic meaning—sudden revelation. Previously, we spoke of acting-out behavior as having a compulsive quality and in terms of its transference significance. Now it is used to describe unexpected behavior of patients during psychotherapy, which may or may not be related to the psychiatrist-patient relationship, and which frequently cannot be documented with any degree of conviction.

The changes in our words and in our thinking, which Dr. Hendrick describes so well, naturally raise a number of questions for which we have no solutions. One might ask, for example, are the changes about which Dr. Hendrick is concerned related to the amount of psychoanalytic theory to which psychiatrists in training have been exposed? Theory that they learned, that they think they understand, but that they understand inadequately and cannot

36

utilize properly in their clinical applications? Armed with the theoretical information they acquire, do our psychiatrists feel less need for the serious and hard work of clinical investigation and that quality of precision in their thinking, that top-notch psychiatry demands? Have we robbed them, so to speak, of some of their scientific curiosity by providing them with so much theoretical knowledge that they acquire intellectually but cannot incorporate with that degree of understanding that one develops during one's personal analysis?

We always remember Freud's statement about understanding, understanding and understanding. We need to ask those in charge of our residency programs how have we been responsible for the problems that concern Dr. Hendrick? We still fall short of the quality of training that cannot even maintain our present-day standards let alone improve them. Dr. Kubie has made valuable suggestions, but I see no effort to implement them, though I think the time is at hand for their implementation. What Dr. Hendrick discusses constitutes a kind of backward drift, something like an undercurrent that invariably accompanies the forward thrust of progress and new knowledge.

Certainly, whenever progress is achieved, something of what was previously valuable becomes discarded only to be recovered at a later time. I refer, for example, to the art of clinical observation, at which Harry Stack Sullivan was adept, and which will always be a valuable instrument for understanding the other person. Adolf Meyer repeatedly admonished his staff that much more could be learned through studying their failures than their successful achievements. Dr. Hendrick has done this very courageously, and his presentation is the first of its kind for inclusion in our scientific literature. He has studied the facts, with which many of us are familiar, but have not discussed in our programs. These problems are not confined to the psychiatrists at Harvard; they are prominent throughout our country. With the passage of more time, I believe that they will increase, that they are fixed patterns of word usage. Seemingly, they cannot be overcome, but we must not continue to add to them unknowingly. Is it not likely that these changes in our words and in our thinking are the changes that we should naturally expect in our psychiatrists who have not had the benefit of analytic training?

I had intended to discuss what I consider the unfortunate aspects of psychopharmacology, but I found Dr. Hendrick's paper so pertinent to our program that I decided to stick to my last. We need, however, always to study both sides of new developments, and the psychotropic drugs present problems that need our attention. They constitute an important tool in our psychiatric armamentarium, and more and more new drugs will be developed. Their use by our psychiatrists of this generation tends to replace the therapeutic use of the self. How this can be avoided is a problem for our discussion at some other meeting. Some of us remember the enormous resistance to the acceptance of psychoanalytic theory prior to World War II, and how this almost vanished in 1945. It is similarly true that psychiatrists stoutly resisted the introduction of the new drugs and then rapidly began using them and abusing them subsequently. These are the psychiatrists of our generation.

2

Psychiatry for Everyman *

PHILIP S. WAGNER, MD

Medical Director, Mental Health Development Center (Subsidiary of Retail Clerks Local 770 and Food Employers Benefit Fund), Los Angeles, Past President, Institute for Psychoanalytic Medicine of Southern California

Labor organizations and their leaders offer promising prospects for community psychiatry. As we make psychiatric services available to low-income and indigent populations, we must ask what modifications must be made and whether these modified practices can be effective. Psychotherapy often must be brief, but this does not preclude an intensive and meaningful involvement between patient and doctor. The relationship to the therapist may be used to catalyze the therapeutic potential of all other relationships. Crisis intervention often assumes increasing importance. The opportunity to achieve psychiatry for every man is excellent, but we do not have the answers, only the prospect of continual effort to identify the areas in which we can be helpful.

PSYCHIATRISTS WHO HAVE SOUGHT to develop community-wide programs during the past several years have been drawn to consider hard, realistic issues with which we psychiatrists are not ordinarily comfortable. We have experienced increasing pressure from consumer groups who seek to include psychiatric services as part of total medical care. We have been confronted by the vacuum of facilities or services for most of the population. We have had again to become students and learn the language and significance of contributions by the epidemiologist, the biostatistician, the social scientist, the medical economist, and even the resources and methods of our new friends in labor organizations.

We have been faced with the problem of financing treatment for middle- and low-income persons who are not members of asso-

* Published here by permission of The William Alanson White Psychiatric Foundation, Inc. See Wagner, Philip S.: "Psychiatry for Everyman," *Psychiatry* *30*:79-90, 1967.

ciations or unions that can develop funds and negotiate for psychiatric services, such as the United Auto Workers, the United States Civil Service Commission, or the California Council of Retail Clerks. The insurance carriers have asked us to correlate diagnosis, cost and duration of treatment, to agree to exclusions that would eliminate their risk, and to provide data on probable utilization rates.

Assuming, despite these problems, that funds are available and some predictive limits on probable cost can be established, we have asked ourselves whether, in order to keep cost at a minimum, new treatment modalities would be required. Critics, even friendly ones, question the effectiveness in the long range of what they suggest may be only second-rate or first-aid psychotherapy.

If, in any event, we can make psychiatric services available to the great numbers of prospective patients from low-income or indigent populations, does the presumably less verbal, less insightful, and less educated patient require special modifications in technique, and if so, what is the nature of these modifications? We are asked, ominously, "What should be the nature of programs and agencies, whether new or modified, that *can* be effective?" [1] (A related question can be raised as to the extent to which residency training in psychiatry prepares clinicians for supplementary techniques, or for flexibility in deviating from what most of us have considered optimal.)

There is no time here, and no time or necessity in our work as clinicians, to engage in polemics. From a five-year experience in developing a variety of psychiatric services and programs in Southern California, I will comment, somewhat categorically and summarily, on the vicissitudes of our efforts to develop community-wide psychiatric services.

Community-Wide Psychiatric Services

1. Factors Affecting Utilization. The education of the eligible population is essential to secure adequate and early utilization. We have used the union newspaper, television, individual mailings, radio, presentations at union meetings, and orientation courses for physicians. Previous educational efforts on the rationale of psychiatric services appeared to have reached a very small percentage of the population. When our program began, about

90% of the Retail Clerk union population thought that psychiatric services were for the insane only. Some of the material made available to the general public has alarming implications, such as the oft-repeated warning: "One out of every ten individuals who read this article will eventually require psychiatric treatment." The content of educational articles should be reassuring and indicate the availability of helpful services, which, of course, should be established before patients are invited to seek psychiatric help.

Referrals by physicians increase as they find through experience that the psychiatrist can be helpful to the physician as well as to the patient. There is a definite increase in utilization when dependents of the employee become eligible. It is easier for parents to bring in a child, even though it may develop that the primary patient is the parent or some other member of the family.

When patients can circumvent application through their physician by *self-referral* or *walk-in,* we found in our experience with the Retail Clerks of Local 770 that utilization increased spectacularly. Since we are convinced of the preventive value of early case finding and early utilization, we search for patients among those who are having medical problems or difficulties in school or at work. We have increased utilization consistently; a plateau has not been reached. In 1965, almost 5% of the Retail Clerk population were seen in the Department of Psychiatry.

On the other hand, contractual limitations lessen utilization. For example, in the case of Federal employees who have a crisis intervention and hospital program, with referral being required by their personal physician, utilization has been at the rate of approximately 2 per 1,000 per year, compared to almost 40 per 1,000 for the Retail Clerks Local 770, whose program has the broadest possible spectrum of readily available psychiatric services, including speech therapy and educational counseling for dependents.

2. *Financing a Psychiatric Program.* The available evidence suggests (insurance carriers tend to guard such data, for competitive purposes, I presume) that for a population of 100,000, a monthly premium of 15 cents could, in the current economy, support adequately a crisis-intervention program consisting of a few outpatient visits and 30 days' hospital treatment, particularly if the insured is required to bear a fraction of the cost. For example, in our Federal program, although 2 per 1,000 may be referred as

probably requiring hospitalization, a few outpatients visits will limit the necessity for hospitalization to about 1 per 1,000, and the number of required hospital days is approximately 25.

A contrasting method of financing, which offers essentially unlimited services, has been developed by the Retail Clerks of Southern California. Employers are required to contribute 2 cents an hour as a fringe benefit to a Welfare Fund, which in the case of Retail Clerks Local 770 makes available more than $500,000 a year for psychiatric services. No limits are set on the amount of outpatient care that can be provided to the employee or dependent, and each patient is entitled to 111 days in-hospital care during any calendar year. This is a fee-for-service program, in contrast to a prepaid insurance program. Services are necessarily limited in a prepaid insurance program, whereas services can be expanded as necessary when the Welfare Fund of a Union accepts responsibility for payment. The evidence accumulates that the financial cost of essential psychiatric services can be estimated with considerable accuracy and that the cost of such services is not prohibitive.[2]

3. *Brief Psychotherapy and the Low Income Patient.* From the beginning, the clinicians in our program had to deal with the problem of reconciling therapeutic goals applicable to a large and diverse patient population with our inability to afford traditional techniques to most and our initial bias that anything less than an intensive therapeutic effort and optimal goals would require a compromise with our professional conscience. Were we of necessity committed to makeshift maneuvers, limited and spurious techniques? Were we to offer our best efforts to a few? Or a palliative but superficial experience to the many?

These questions are by this time academic. The spectrum of "brief psychotherapies" includes specific modalities applicable to specific problems. "Brief" psychotherapy may be neither brief nor superficial nor preclude an intensive and meaningful involvement between patient and doctor. Our own practice is to assist the patient through a stressful period and make it possible for him to return when he again feels the need for further clarification or support. Neither the therapist nor the patient need consider a termination as final, therefore, nor if there are residual symptoms and problems to consider his therapeutic experience a failure.

Male, 19, requested emergency assistance in connection with his feeling that he might "crack up." Precipitating incident was rejection by his 15½-year-old girlfriend, regarding whom he had both idealized and premature expectations as well as sexual fantasies, any satisfaction of which would require a mutual commitment of loyalty and eventually marriage. Obviously shaken by the rejection, the patient expressed fear that his girlfriend would become promiscuous or emotionally disturbed.

At the intitial interview, patient agreed that he was confused about his sexual feelings and in reality was unable to assume responsibility for an unstable adolescent companion. During the turmoil of this relationship he continued his employment as a retail clerk, but was progressively failing in his scholastic work as a college freshman.

Between the first and second sessions, patient inflicted a superficial laceration on his left wrist and showed this to his girlfriend, who responded as he hoped, by acting grief-stricken and remorseful. His own turmoil subsided almost at once. He slept well, and immediately began dating other girls. On his second visit, he still expressed an interest in helping his friend with her emotional problems, but accepted the statement that his illness was our primary concern and that he was too sick to provide emotional support to his friends. Before his third visit, he again visited his girlfriend, who thoroughly berated and swore at him, following which he shifted his attention to the girlfriend's roommate. Patient related his current reaction of grief and anger to his early experiences of his parents' quarrels, but this connection and reference seemed at the time in the nature of "textbook insight."

The evident hostility towards women based on his recent experience and former relationships with girls was introduced to qualify his protestations regarding his idealized intentions. By the time of his third visit, his anger and desire for either an idealized or mutually destructive resolution was no longer evident. Patient was encouraged to defer further intensive involvements with girls until he felt able to cope with his own expectations and confused feelings. He was seen for a few additional visits, first twice a month then once.

One year later, patient returned, expressing acute anxiety and ambivalence about the prospect of induction into military service. He felt that he needed time to reflect on the meaning of such a complete abrogation of his own convictions. He affiliated with a church that, on religious grounds, supported his wish for deferment of his military obligations, and the clinic was able to provide sufficient data to assist in deferment of military service. As a result of his anxiety, he withdrew from school and from work. Once deferment was assured, he returned to full-time work in an industry that he felt gave him more status, and made plans to save money and return to school the following fall.

He continues to be seen on a walk-in basis, about once every three months. He considers these visits as access to a friend for advice regarding his activities and plans. His work performance has been satisfactory, his relationship with his parents is now amicable, and there has been no evidence that he continues to seek the idealized love relationship as a means of resolving his characteristic adolescent problems.

The case illustrates the ability of an adolescent to use "brief" assistance during transitional and characteristic adolescent crises, without the need for extensive or intensive "relationship" or "uncovering" therapy.

If we hold a patient in treatment after symptomatic relief, we may cause him to believe that the therapist is not yet satisfied, and can be satisfied only by disclosure of more psychopathology and attitudes of regression and dependency. This may be an essential experience for a patient in psychoanalytic psychotherapy, but in clinic practice the patient may feel confused if he is not released after the presenting problem has been resolved or relieved.

Most psychotherapy should be brief, not because there is a long clinic waiting list, or because the patient cannot afford intensive treatment, but out of deference to the realistic economic limitations of both the patient's circumstances and those of the clinic that provides care. A realistic acceptance of the need for economy of time and effort in working toward desired goals is a high art applicable to all human endeavor, and particularly in psychotherapy, where the patient tends to mark time while opportunity and years pass him by. The acknowledgment of such realistic limitations encourages the patient towards self-reliance rather than dependency, once the immediate crisis has lessened.

4. The Emergency Aspects of the Appeal for Help. Despite all efforts to encourage early utilization, most patients present themselves in what they regard as a state of emergency, although it usually is not. The referral to the psychiatrist is often seen, by the referring physician or the family, as a final and desperate measure. With most patients, the psychiatrist's passive involvement—with patient, family, or referring physician—will be taken as evidence of incompetence or noninterest. Relief often follows the demonstrated interest and activity of the therapist. Traditional silence or expectant waiting for a patient's associations is something for which all clinic patients are unprepared and find confusing.

Marital couple, both about 60 years old, referred by an internist who had been treating both for hyperthyroidism and hypertension over several years. It was his impression that their marriage was soon to terminate, after bitter and seemingly irreconcilable recriminations regarding their relationships at work and problems with their children.

Seen together, they politely agreed that they had no mutual interests, were in constant conflict on all issues, allowed themselves no social or recreational outlets, felt burdened by the problems of their children, and no longer had any sexual life. Despite this grim picture, there was an element of congeniality and agreement regarding their importance to each other, which suggested a favorable prognosis for the marriage.

Seen alone, Mr. described a life of unceasing hard work and acknowledged that this contributed to his wife's feeling of deprivation. He has the European point of view that a woman should be silent and servile. Mrs., seen separately, gave a history of an early family life in which she was overburdened by the need to assist her mother in caring for 9 children, married early to be relieved of this burden, then felt guilty for abandoning her mother. She is pervasively guilty about everything. She feels she was never able to give her children or her husband sufficient affection. She has had recurrent anxiety for years, stemming undoubtedly from her ambivalence and covert hostility.

Mrs. was seen individually because of her anxiety, tearfulness, and apparent feeling of desperation, related to her inability to cope with the marital conflict or with a successive series of problems with children and grandchildren. After several sessions over a period of three months, during which she ventilated her accumulated grievances toward her husband, and her use of the marriage as a relationship on to which she could project the many anxieties and conflicts associated with symptoms characteristic of a dependent hysteric person, her symptoms subsided, her feelings of guilt decreased, and she was able to resume a less emotional and more amicable working relationship with her husband.

At her insistence, Mr. was seen for several sessions. His compulsive work schedule and dissociation from the problems of the marriage and his children, with its attendant guilt, were reviewed. The psychiatrist's tactics were intended to avoid identifying Mr. as in a "patient" role, but rather as a peer who had been dealing valiantly and quite successfully with extensive lifelong marital and family problems. Mr. and Mrs. were then seen jointly, and a more realistic evaluation and appreciation of each other's difficulties was possible. The sessions focused primarily on their feelings of guilt and inadequacy that, despite great effort, both their children had evolved as psychopathic individuals. Both children, although more than thirty years of age, were still attempting to exploit their parents financially and emotionally. The focus of work shifted quickly to the problems of these adult "children" and finally to the grandchild, for whom they had assumed complete responsibility. The shift in emphasis, from preoccupation with their marital problems and assistance in their conscientious effort as parents, appeared to move the relationship from one of constant recrimination to a collaborative effort regarding their personal needs and those of the children. Mr's symptoms of headache, presumably related to hypertension, appeared to decrease in severity as the more immediate problems were resolved in the course of therapy. Mrs. had a thyroidectomy, which was effective in reducing symptoms that originally had been attributed to anxiety and menopausal changes. There was no further need for psychiatric services during a follow-up period of two years.

The case illustrates the inappropriateness of attempting to isolate the individual problem from those of the family or from the organic and medical problems that require continued management. As is our custom, we do not "terminate," but remain available to the primary patient and various other members of the family. In the present situation, the psychopathic son was seen and encouraged to move out of the family home with his transient girlfriends, and the parents were relieved of guilt that by agreeing to his separation from the home they were remiss in their responsibilities to their children.

5. *Contribution of Realistic Stress, Including Multiple Family Pathology.* Situational, realistic, and somatic problems complicate the psychological. In most patients, we see evidence of chronic fatigue in both the individual and his family. We see the effect of years of chronic frustration, of apprehension concerning the continued ability to hold a job, the attrition of marginal economic subsistence, and the slow exhaustion from chronic medical problems. These are for the patient the harsh realities. He requires evidence that they are acknowledged, even though he is convinced that they cannot be altered.

6. *The Therapeutic Potential in All Relationships.* Intensive psychotherapy is based on the hypothesis that the therapeutic relationship is fundamental and paramount. Brief therapy does not

discount the sometimes dramatic and always remembered encounter with the therapist. In psychoanalytic and other intensive therapies, the relationship with the therapist is considered the sine qua non. In brief psychotherapy, the relationship may be scrutinized as illustrative of other interpersonal experiences, but the patient is not taken through the "fires of transference." The intent is rather to catalyze the potential for more meaningful experience in all other relationships. By involving the other family members, friends, or the referring physician as allies in the therapeutic effort, the psychotherapist need not be the sole bulwark in the patient's effort to find reinstatement and satisfaction as a social being.

7. *The Egosyntonic Effect of "Defense Mechanisms".* The patient's ability for spontaneous improvement, the innate tendency for self-repair, tends to be underestimated when we emphasize the process of recovery as dependent primarily on the therapeutic experience. Patients do get well spontaneously, and the zealous therapist may interfere with this process. Clinic patients frequently do better with the therapist who is less eager to find pathology, or whose therapeutic expectations are more limited, than with those who are overly preoccupied with the patient's psychopathology and feel impelled to designate most findings as regressive, or infantile, or symptomatic. In addition, we need to remember that a neurotic or psychosomatic defense may be life saving, or at least preferable to the acknowledgment of some painful reality, either external or unconscious, that cannot be changed.

8. *The Capacity to Endure When Circumstances Are Unalterable.* Assisting the patient to "endure" is not just an effort to support or reconcile him to the inevitable. I think of it rather as a learning to live *with* or *despite* the problem. The rationale for this approach is our awareness that the creation of "problems" is also a product of the patient's unconscious needs. An inappropriate or overdetermined reaction to *realistic* problems may be evidence of projection and displacement, through which the patient attempts to deal with *suppressed* problems and affects. The external problem may be nurtured even though the patient may protest, "I can't live with it—or live with it this way". But clarification of contributing peripheral stress may sustain the patient in his effort to endure seemingly unalterable distress, either organic or situational.

Comprehensive and coordinated psychiatric and medical management for elderly patients must be provided. Employees who retire and suffer the escalating problems of medical illness and incapacity for self-management require a multi-disciplined approach in order to postpone regressive deterioration and custodial care. Such patients require active intervention and cannot be relied on to seek psychiatric assistance on their own initiative.

A woman of 65, following brief hospitalization for "agitated depression," complained that her 75-year-old husband was insulting, rejecting, and critical of her, that he had now decided to stay in bed at home and starve himself to death, and that his business affairs were chaotic. The patient was characteristically obsessed with money, with the loss of her husband's affection and his interest in young girls, and with her bowels. Despite the apparent paranoid element in the patient's concerns, social work investigation revealed that her husband attributed his wife's depression to his expressed interest in an 18-year-old secretary, and that he had, indeed, reached a degree of senile depression and discouragement that justified the patient's concerns as realistic. Patient was indignant that a former therapist had suggested that her preoccupation with her husband's erotic interests was a projection of her own erotic longings. Her evaluation of her previous therapist as impatient and impersonal also had a realistic basis, since such a patient confronts the therapist with his limitations, with the irritation evoked by a querulous and complaining patient and the seemingly insolvable plight of aged couples.

The psychiatrist undertook to solicit the interest of other members of the family, to use the union organization to clarify the confused management of finances, to persuade a visiting nurse to evaluate conditions at home, to collaborate with the attending physician, and to prepare this couple for eventual residence in a nursing home. This retired employee has access to such coordinated care, since the union that subsidizes the medical-psychiatric program accepts responsibility for the worker after termination of his usefulness as an employee.

9. Indications for Termination. When the presenting complaint or problem is relieved, most clinic patients see no reason for continued treatment, and most clinic situations do not justify such continued individual psychotherapy. Even though theoretically we may assume that we have only increased the patient's defenses and that although he is now feeling and functioning more satisfactorily his gains may be temporary, nevertheless, we have reached the goal that the patient, and frequently his family, feel is sufficient.

Male union employee, aged 56, requested emergency consultation following a sudden onset of acute anxiety in connection with driving on the Los Angeles freeways. The precipitating event was his attendance at the funeral of an old friend who had died of coronary heart disease. Patient had had cardiac angina for two years prior to onset of present complaint. For several months, he had felt vaguely depressed and discouraged, despite continued and effective performance at work. Because his work required the use of an automobile, temporarily impossible because of his severe anxiety, he was placed on medical disability.

This patient had always been obsessively dedicated to his work and periodically anxious when he felt he was not performing according to his own high self-expectations, or those required by his employer. Therapy was directed toward a lessening of his standards for work performance, affirmation of his ability to continue work by bringing in evidence from employers and co-workers, and discussion of the wish to withdraw from his responsibilities through illness or a suicidal resolution. He gradually began driving in the company of friends and co-workers, and in the course of two months the driving phobia subsided. The original symptom was replaced by a phobia of having his hair cut, which gradually lessened as he shared his anxiety with his barber, who reassured him by cutting the patient's hair "after hours" and by not using a razor. There was no attempt to explore the dynamics of the "castration anxiety" other than to identify his masochistic need to seek punishment because of his inability to perform at a level he had maintained for more than 20 years. Antidepressive medication appeared to have little more than suggestive effect. Patient requested return to full employment three months after his initial contact.

One year later, he reported a return of his driving phobia, but continued at work without limitation. At this time, his apprehensions since childhood about disease or injury were discussed. Minimal medication with a mild tranquilizer and reassurance appeared sufficient for effective reduction of symptoms. Patient stated that he found considerable reassurance from ready access, on a walk-in basis, to his psychiatrist. Subsequently, for a two-year period until the end of 1966, he was fully preoccupied with his responsibility at work, but on two occasions arranged a "social" visit on an informal walk-in basis.

The case illustrates that clarification of contributing circumstances and reassurance were sufficient to keep this valuable employee at work. It is doubtful that any effort at exploration in depth of his "castration anxiety" would have provided a more meaningful or effective therapeutic experience. In any event, the outcome of the treatment experience indicated that "brief psy-chotherapy" was sufficient.

Impressions of "Low Income" Patients that Do Not Support Some Standard Conceptions

1. The Fee. The payment of a fee by clinic patients neither lessens nor enhances motivation or dependency, nor does it influ-ence the length of treatment, except that the inability to pay acts as a deterrent.

2. The Diagnosis. Excepting the psychoses, there is little appar-ent correlation between the diagnosis, using the APA classifica-tion, and the time and cost of treatment to the point of significant relief from symptoms. The more meaningful criteria are the dura-tion of the illness, the degree of disability, the evidence of concur-rent medical dependency and hypochondriasis, and the presence of contributing social or family problems.

3. Socioeconomic Status. We have not found socioeconomic status a useful indication of a patient's ability to use psychother-apy. Psychological inaccessibility, limited verbal ability and lack of motivation also occur in upper class, high-income patients. The more important factors appear to be the reality of the individual's experience that has made for a varying degree of distrust, and the reality of the therapist's personal accessibility and/or conscious or unconscious resistance to accept and involve himself in the pa-tient's problems. When the unsophisticated person learns that psychiatry offers a wide range of help for personal problems, his rate of utilization is not appreciably different from that of the more sophisticated middle-class patient.

Woman of 42 was referred for psychiatric evaluation following ten years of medical management for intermittent hypochon-driacal complaints. Patient was evaluated as "a deprived and impoverished person who, with the exception of a brief period in her life when she went away with a man and had a chance to express herself and achieve some gratification, has been more or less a steady workhorse and feels that there is really not much else she is cut out for. She is trying to provide her daughters with some advantages of more cultured and privileged existence, but really sees little future for herself. The prognosis for her continu-ing in this limited mode of adjustment is probably fairly high. The chances of any real change . . . are not too good. If the husband is amenable to some work with the two of them, it might be possible to help them make their marriage slightly more gratifying."

Patient expressed distrust and skepticism regarding psychiatric service. Discussion of her problem, she felt, would not alter her life situation. She expressed reluctance at including the husband in the psychiatric evaluation and was resentful that he had for years urged her to seek psychiatric consultation.

Mr., 46, described a progressively deteriorating family situation, long-standing differences with his wife regarding management of the children and progressive concern about his own ability to carry on for an indefinite period as a provider for his family.

An interview with their son, 21, confirmed the fact of constant quarreling at home, but he believed that basically his parents were "still in love with each other." He described his father as rigid and very old-fashioned, but sincere, hard-working and "really a likeable old fellow," though exhausted on Sundays and unable to join in family activities. He believed that his parents had never had a social or recreational life, but were primarily preoccupied with their interpersonal frustrations.

In individual sessions, the patient's passive resistance and unwittingly revealed contempt for her husband were elicited. The therapist took the position that she had in fact undermined her husband's efforts and had attempted to isolate him from his children. Seen separately, her husband's attitude toward the family was characterized to him as dictatorial, and the difference in expectations derived from his own Germanic background and those of the adolescent in the American culture was discussed. He resented the description of his posture at home as "Prussian," but evidently yielded to the authoritarian judgment of his psychiatrist and made a sincere attempt to involve himself more personally at home and to be more revealing of his basic affectionate concerns.

As a result of this "corrective" confrontation, the marriage again seemed to settle into a relatively satisfactory status. Two years after our initial contact with this family, the patient's husband applied for further service, stating that the issues that concerned him at this time were not those for which he and his wife had requested consultation previously. The parents were now concerned about the status of their two daughters. One was described as excessively shy and progressively isolated, the other as participating with the mother in effecting an antagonistic split within the family. Mrs. again doubted the effectiveness of psychiatric service and continued to deny that either of the daughters required psychiatric evaluation or assistance. She viewed them as constitutionally predisposed toward opposite personality types. Six months later, Mr. made a desperate appeal for immediate consultation regarding the youngest daughter, who continued to show signs of social withdrawal and academic failure, despite good intelligence and many years of education in music, which she had intended to follow as a profession. Mrs. then conceded that perhaps her younger daughter did require help, and individual treatment for the child was arranged. Following our recommendation that the child required counseling, both parents appeared relieved and the home situation again became relatively tranquil and amicable.

The case illustrates the characteristic reluctance of the mother to acknowledge that either she or her children might require specialized help, and the relief that follows when parents nevertheless accept such help and see in their child a favorable response. We are impressed with the frequency with which marital discord is lessened and parents can deal with each other more realistically, when a psychiatric problem within the family can finally be acknowledged and help is accepted.

4. The Effective Psychotherapist. Competence as a psychotherapist is not related to the therapist's discipline: the social worker, psychologist or psychiatric nurse can be as effective as or more effective than the physician. The effective therapist responds with a low degree of anxiety in the face of severe psychopathology, hostility and poverty. He perceives, if only intuitively, the significant intrapsychic and interpersonal dynamics. A degree of masochistic and even "messianic" motivation may assist the therapist in enduring the daily confrontation of diverse and severe psychopathology. Many of our therapists are familiar through childhood experience with the problems of low-income patients, and perhaps some of their motivation derives from a continual working through of residual anxieties from this experience. As Dr. Lewis Hill observed, we repeatedly work through segments of our personal analysis in our analytical experience with patients. The more important therapeutic factors that provide relief are: *a.* the therapist's ability to respond to the patient with interest and insight, *b.* the reduction of the patient's projected distortions, which evoke "paranoid" anxiety, and *c.* the patient's growing awareness of alternative and more appropriate reactions to his problem, both emotional and adaptive.

5. Medical Dependency and Psychiatric Utilization. Families that use medical services extensively can be classified into two groups: *a.* those that seek to resolve personal problems through hypochondriacal dependency, and *b.* those that, because of greater education or sophistication, actively use medical services to which they are entitled as an insurance benefit, in the interest of "good medical care." The latter group uses psychiatric services for the same reasons when such a benefit is made available through the health program.

Most patients in the former group, once they are exposed to psychiatric service, soon recognize their hypochondriasis as a rationalization for emotional or interpersonal problems. In this group there are, of course, the confirmed somatically preoccupied individuals who seek medical or psychiatric services for the nurturing and reassurance that they are unable to achieve in realistic human relationships.

6. Limitations on Length of Treatment. A limitation on "time" can compel the patient and therapist to make adequate and intensive use of time—provided the therapist is not hindered by resentment towards such limitations. Most of these patients and their families have no intellectualized preconceptions about the time required, the objectives of treatment, and the like. The problem therefore is primarily the therapist's—a matter of his ability to set limited goals rather than to pursue the idealized goals suggested by his training or by his personal therapeutic experience.

7. Resistance to Utilization: Is the Patient Motivated? The apprehension or bias about the use of psychiatric services is effectively overcome by continually and intelligibly educating the entire community, including physicians. Patients eventually accept psychiatric services in the same manner that they accept the specialized help of other medical specialists. Having access to a psychiatrist is a status symbol in Beverly Hills, and becomes similarly valued by the working man and his family.

After the decision to reorganize the union psychiatric program in a new facility, it became administratively necessary to discontinue psychiatric services in one of our outlying facilities. As a result, a patient complained to the Executive Secretary of the union.

Dear Mr.——:
The need for consolidation of the psychiatric services in the Union Headquarters can perhaps be demonstrated, though this would work a hardship for the membership in . . . , who would

have to travel a great distance to Union Headquarters for weekly (and sometimes bi-weekly) therapy.

Providing new doctors for us to continue our therapy at Union Headquarters is not enough. We are not being treated for the common cold or a toothache. The nature of our difficulties and the nature of the psychiatric curative process demands the same doctor over a period of time. Why not just transfer these doctors and their patients to the new facilities if it is absolutely necessary but why fire the staff of the . . . facility and jeopardize the recovery of their patients?

My family and I have been very grateful for the psychiatric services of the Union as we have had to use these services in recent years. We think they are very fine as they are. And we commend you for your forward looking approach to union benefits in this area. We trust you will not forget us in . . . , who need this facility and these doctors.

Sincerely,

8. *The Stigma of Psychiatric Illness.* We found that the fear of stigma and loss of self-esteem or status in the relationship with family, friends, or employers is usually based on the patient's projected distortions. Family and friends almost invariably support a patient in his efforts to secure help. Employer resistance is not conspicuous, once a program has been established through labor-management negotiations. Employers are realistic and prefer to see an effective use of the funds they contribute.

9. *Psychiatric Treatment and the Job.* There is no evidence that the patient's work eligibility or circumstances are jeopardized by the fact that he is receiving psychiatric treatment. However, occasionally the patient's work situation may be altered by his employer's response to the behavior that the patient's own psychological problems bring about. Such patients, therefore, may be assigned to less favorable working hours, or they may not be used at the times when overtime pay is offered, as on weekends or nights.

10. *"Quality" Facilities and Their Effect on Patients.* Treatment facilities found pleasant to the middle-class patient are equally appreciated by all patients. One does not have to see the patient in a shabby or neglected facility so that he will "feel at ease." Whether laborer or upper-class individual, the patient's uneasiness relates primarily to his anxiety about forthcoming interviews or the presence in the waiting room of other people with whom he is customarily ill at ease.

Social Impact of the Community Mental Health Center

1. *The Need for Organizational and Technical Flexibility.* A psychiatric organization has a style, a philosophy, and techniques that are developed in response to the requirements of the community of potential patients. This is as it should be, quite as we adapt our techniques to the requirements of the individual patient. We are long past the early child-guidance model with the evaluation of the problem of the patient by each of three disciplines, the staff case conference, then the inevitable waiting period before assignment, and the expectation of an indefinitely prolonged involvement with the patient. This model may still be appropriate for some teaching and research institutions, but the community clinic must be a flexible and accommodating organization, responsive to the socioeconomic characteristics of the community in which it is located, and capable of changes in staff structure and techniques as it learns the characteristics of the population it serves.

When we started our program in 1961, we had the immediate obligation, as a specialty clinic within a medical complex, to secure clinicians who had sufficient experience to require a minimal amount of supervision and who could provide the standard diagnostic evaluation and initiate or recommend appropriate treatment. We needed a senior psychiatrist to provide a supplementary evaluation that would confirm or modify the intake diagnostic evaluation, and to give medical sanction and supervision to the patient's treatment. As our case load increased, we found that our earlier hope for a concurrent and collaborative family evaluation—which would consider not only the patient's intrapsychic and interpersonal problems but also his response to his milieu, whether family, school or work, and our own growing understanding of such psychosocial factors—progressively waned. A few among us undertook family evaluation, group therapy, collaborative treatment of marital pairs or parent-adolescent problems. Eventually, however, our clinicians began to work essentially as individual practitioners with their own private practice in the clinic setting, and in the main, tended to revert to their early coping mechanisms. This is not to say that they were not helpful and often effective, but in many instances they were not "on target"—for example, in working intensively with a child when the family situation was essentially psychotic, or with a chronically depressed patient when he was slowly but effectively being demeaned in a mutually destructive marriage relationship.

Repeatedly, we found that if we looked *around* the patient at the parent, spouse, job or community, contributing factors appeared that were more important, and more immediately accessible, than the patient's dependency needs, transference ambivalence, or residual developmental anxieties. Not that these latter issues could always be unattended, but they seldom were of primary and immediate importance, and their emergence was frequently a defensive reponse to intolerable current issues. We reached a point where we found ourselves reluctant to diagnose an individual patient without an interview with the spouse or other immediate members of the family, and without access to the written longitudinal medical record. For example, a woman's attitude to herself as wife and mother may become strikingly vivid if we meet with her and her children, on another occasion with her husband and children, and still on another occasion in her home.

Within the confines of the clinic, there is opportunity for creative ingenuity. For example, two of our social workers decided to concentrate on the problems of the "illegitimately" pregnant girl and the indignant or ashamed mother. Working separately with their patients, they found that frequently the mother has been through the same experience of an illegitimate pregnancy. Subsequent confrontation between mother and daughter can eventually result in a tearful rapprochement between the two. Frequently a mother may insist that father would kill somebody if he knew of his daughter's condition. Father is almost always, in fact, more forgiving and accepting—unless he is overwhelmed by fear of his angry wife. To psychoanalysts, the dynamics of these intrafamilial events are well understood, and they attempt to understand with the patient the unconscious determinants of her dilemma and wait for a solution to emerge. But therapists seeking to resolve a crisis or avoid a catastrophe find that an evaluation of, and confrontation between, the persons involved seems increasingly, as we gain experience, more expeditious and effective.

2. *Objectives of the Community Mental Health Center.* The establishment of a mental health center by no means ensures the development of an adequate community psychiatric program. A wide variation exists in the mutual accessibility and mutual un-

derstanding of those who would help and those who need help. For example, we were certain that adolescents in our eligible community (Retail Clerks, Local 770) did not make full use of our services. Therefore, we developed a facility separate from the psychiatric clinic or from any treatment modality that might place the adolescent in the role of a psychiatric patient, and headlined services that adolescents understand, such as vocational and educational counseling. In this program, we keep the psychiatrist "off stage" but available in the "wings."

By early 1964, we felt pleased with the evidence that we had effectively achieved the integration of medical and psychiatric services in a group health agency.[3] The desired features of a community mental health center—collaboration between referring physician and psychiatrist, the easy availability of medical data, the continuity of medical-psychiatric-hospital and outpatient clinic care, the increasing acceptance by our medical colleagues— had been a rewarding experience. We became increasingly uneasy, however, as we discussed our relative isolation from the union organization and population and as we recognized the tendency towards use of our services primarily for diagnosis, crisis intervention and hospital management. Utilization had indeed increased, but the medical "model" resulted in the growing concern by some of us that although we had established ourselves as a medical specialty, we had not fully explored our potential within the union-social organization, nor had we taken full advantage of the union's leadership and generous financing in developing a community psychiatric program.

We have at this time decided to take our union program out of the medical complex and establish a facility and program within the union organization. An assortment of technical services can be provided in a community mental health center, but a comprehensive psychiatric program requires an aggressive extension into the community of services and activities not conventionally considered "clinical", despite—and even because of—language barriers, ethnic differences, distance and inaccessibility by public transportation, and the gross realities of community disintegration and economic hardship. Any token involvement will not suffice. A major intrusion, active involvement, mutual education, and an eventual proprietary identification by the community of potential patients are our goals.

We want to explore the effect of acting as union psychiatrists rather than as medical specialists in a Group Health Association. A union psychiatrist can consider time spent with a business agent or shop steward, with a probation officer or school counselor, as a useful and essential service. The cost accounting department of an insurance company may have doubts that this is a measurable, predictable, or in any sense a necessary "clinical" service. The medical model augments the clinician's tendency to think in terms of disease, course of illness, and degree of cure. The social-welfare model of a union directs our attention to the feasibility of helpful involvement in many aspects of family life, work and individual experience that can hardly, and need not, be identified as clinical problems.

It must certainly be evident that I see our labor organizations and their leaders as providing the most promising prospects for community psychiatry. I know your high regard for the leadership and funds provided by Federal agencies in your neighboring city. But Los Angeles is 3,000 miles away, and Watts is a million miles away, and Federal funds create in due, but excessive time, great facilities, and great administrative costs, and tend to perpetuate in their facilities a therapeutic climate and decor that is too close for my taste to the rows of clinic benches I remember at Bellevue, that established patients as supplicants rather than as deserving persons. Having worked in almost every Government medical service except the Peace Corps, I agree to that extent with the concerns of the American Medical Association. But labor leaders cannot allow their constituents to feel abandoned or depersonalized, else they will no longer be labor leaders.

What are the prospects of psychiatry, in its broadest sense, for Everyman? Considerable, I believe. But they point to no clear goal as to our potential participation or usefulness, and offer only the prospect of continual effort and the identification of areas of human experience where we can be helpful. We are going through a phase of great opportunity, but also of great disenchantment among a few individuals who have overrated our ability to bring heaven on earth. A patient of mine said, "But I thought you were Jesus." My unfriendly response was, "Perhaps I am." I should have said that perhaps at one time I thought I was, and possibly this lack of self-critical humility has expelled us from heaven, so that now we are properly back in the rank and file of the many who feel that we still have much to learn. But if we can add humility to our proved resourcefulness, we need not feel discouraged. As Harry Stack Sullivan often said: We can consider ourselves successful if we achieve 51% of what we set ourselves to do.

REFERENCES

1. Rae-Grant, Q. A., Gladwin, T., and Bower, E. M.: Mental health, social competence, and the war on poverty, Amer J Orthopsychiat *36*:652-664 (Aug), 1966.

2. US Department of Health, Education and Welfare: Improving Mental Health Insurance Coverage, Washington (DC), US Government Printing Office, August, 1965.

3. Wagner, P. S.: Integrated Medical and Psychiatric Services in a Group Health Agency, unpublished paper presented at International Congress of Social Psychiatry, London, August, 1964. (*Available from Mental Health Development Center, 1515 No. Vermont Ave., Los Angeles, Calif. 90027.*)

Discussion

JOEL ELKES, MD

Henry Phipps Professor of Psychiatry and Director, Department of Psychiatry and Behavioral Sciences, The Johns Hopkins University, Psychiatrist-in-Chief, The Johns Hopkins Hospital, Baltimore

DR. GIBSON HAS CONSTRUCTED the program most carefully, for Dr. Hendrick, discussed by Dr. Bartemeier, has anticipated the very issues that Dr. Wagner has raised so freshly, humanly, and humanely. Dr. Hendrick spoke of the way in which words and concepts are apt to imprison us, the way they create a verbal armor in which we strut about like medieval knights, heavied down, defended, and unable to move. He also suggested the opposite: namely, the way words change, and evolve, the way they can fashion, as well as immobilize, concepts. For good or ill, words are potent things; and science is but the history of the languages of science. I think it was Thomas Huxley who said that science begins with heresy, advances to orthodoxy, and ends up in superstition. We have more than our fair share of orthodoxy and superstition in psychiatry: and some travel in the guises of "models," ancient and out of date though they may be.

Dr. Wagner is no purveyor of "models." He talks of actual experience and compels a rethinking of old habits. I am sorry not to have seen Dr. Wagner's chapter until only a short while ago, and I can do no better than to go through the headings that compose his strong thesis.

He started with the assumption that we must give service to all, and that there may be ways of arranging for the economics of such service. He gave us the startling figure that for 15 cents for a population of 100,000 in the current economy, one could support a crisis intervention program, and for somewhat higher figures, one could allow actual regular consultation. He also made the point, right from the beginning, that utilization depends on the

60

way one initially approaches (and the language one uses in approaching) patients and the way one presents the problem to them, in terms of general need. He stressed the fact that the walk-in clinic is, in some instances, more useful than referral clinics; and then he went on to develop his thesis in terms of the economy of the time of service, and of "brief psychotherapy," which "may be neither brief nor superficial, nor does it preclude an intensive and meaningful involvement between patient and doctor." He states, "Our own practice is to assist the patient through stressful periods and make it possible for him to return when he again feels the need for further clarification or support. Neither the therapist nor the patient, therefore, needs to consider a termination as final." He stresses the value of the emergency intervention, and he again states that *involvement* in the crisis situation is important since the silence and expectant waiting of the traditional analytic situation are not understood by clinic patients. He stresses the need for realistic intervention in crisis situations, and then speaks of the therapeutic potential in *all* relationships. The patient need not necessarily be "taken through the fires of transference." He can, in fact, transfer to objects and persons in his own environment, provided there is someone to guide him through these multiple social transactions that are true transferences. There is meaningful experience in all relationships. He goes on to look at the way in which "nature" takes a hand; he stresses that there is such a thing as spontaneous improvement, and that the zealous therapist may interfere with this process. He emphasizes the capacity to endure and the capacity to learn, from experience.

And finally, he questions certain assumptions: first, the fee, which in his experience neither lessens nor enhances motivation; then, the value of the minutiae of diagnoses, which he feels may not be the best or the most helpful labels; then the assumption that socioeconomic status precludes some psychotherapy or modified psychotherapy; then again, the tacit (and somewhat arrogant) assumption that the therapist's competence is necessarily related to the therapist's discipline.

It is evident that effective psychotherapy is not a medical prerogative. The social worker, the psychologist, or the suitably trained psychiatric nurse may indeed be very effective. Lastly, he goes on to develop his emphasis on the *health* rather than the *disease model,* the need for true prevention, for keeping in touch with the touchstone of normality. Indeed, it would appear that his own personal experience has been sufficiently convincing to wish to move a preventive service away from a hospital setting. Are there profound implications for the location for some of our mental health agencies in what he says? If we fused Crisis Counseling Centers and Clinics with Neighborhood and Family-Life Centers, rather than hospitals, would we render better service, numerically and qualitatively? Only experience will tell. Brick and mortar have a way of encasing people. Should one not scatter rather than create new massive physical structures? The mental health centers being formed now will have profound consequences because, by providing therapeutic facilities for a variety of patients, irrespective of socioeconomic background, they are bound to enlarge, as Dr. Wagner indicated, the concept of psychotherapy itself.

This process is often thought of in terms of long-term verbal therapy; that is, talking and listening things through on a regular basis. But communication by words is not the only way in which people communicate. Indeed, some patients may be incapable of communication by words; their vocabulary may be too limited, their anger too fierce, their upbringing stressing action rather than words. One could call this *communication by doing*. And such communication requires a totally new range of skills or, to be more precise, a cultivation or addition of well-established skills, and particularly those he mentioned: vocational experimental work programs, educational therapy, work in small groups, with family, with employers and educators. It requires continuous consultation with the therapist in an atmosphere not merely of the conventional professional relationship but of engaged and actual commitment and responsibility. People, by and large, will respond to expectations provided they are conveyed in a relationship of trust. It is remarkable what people will do provided the trust is there, provided they are given the chance for human contact and practical guidance. Trust, like peace, is indivisible. Patients and therapists invariably share in this process of growth.

Here Dr. Wagner brings us to another opportunity. It is evident that we will need many more people in the mental health field. But what people? With what skills? How selected? Trained for what? Trained where, by whom? No doubt we will be able to count on the expansion of the existing professions and the skilled and highly trained persons—psychologists, social workers, occupational therapists, educational therapists, vocational rehabilitation officers—but will this be enough? And what of other resources? It seems to me that there are two such major potential resources available to us. One is the young people selected for their proven ability to deal with difficult human relationships and with unforeseen handicaps and adversities. The other is a more mature group who, having successfully overcome the handicaps and adversities in their own lives, and having raised families, are now looking for ways of being useful to their fellow men.

The Peace Corps has shown us what remarkable results can be achieved by careful selection following practical training and wise guidance in the field. It is quite evident that resourcefulness and emotional maturity are not the prerogatives of age, but can be fostered by intense yet thoroughly practical learning experience. Would it not be wise, therefore, for us to think in similar terms in mental health? Should we not learn from the selection and training procedures of the Peace Corps and aim at developing a type of Social Therapist or Mental Health Counselor who—say, after two years of junior college—could learn by being trained and involved in Therapy-by-Doing, by relating, by facing, by example? Could we not train others intensely in therapeutic counseling? Such ideas may be worth exploring; and our own good experience with college students working at the Phipps Clinic encourages me in this direction even more.

Another resource of great potential is represented by our women citizens who, having established a home and successfully raised a family, are free to put their native and practical knowledge to use in helping others over mental handicap or emotional difficulty. You may know that five years ago the NIMH furthered a small pilot project,[1] which involved eight trainees in a two-year program, to train mental health counselors. This program was thoroughly practical in nature, case-oriented rather than theory-oriented. Theory *followed* practical work. It aimed at developing therapeutic skills that could be used (always, of course, under medical supervision) in a clinic, a hospital, or any other suitable setting. I confess at this point that I am not an entirely impartial judge of this program. My wife, Dr. Charmian Elkes, and Dr. Margaret Rioch were co-principal investigators in the program at the NIMH. But I can say that one's skepticism some four years ago is now, in the light of the experience, turning into an equally cautious optimism. The fact is that after two years of training, and three years of subsequent follow-up with no assurance whatever as to job (much less to job satisfaction), all trainees are sought after and in paid and satisfying employment. We are starting a similar program at the Phipps Clinic under the formal aegis of the Johns Hopkins Hospital and we will see how we go.

It is clear, in any event, that we have to look to other resources than we have. This looking to other resources is bound to take us away from the disease model. Such counterpoint is much needed. In fact, as I listened to Dr. Wagner, I felt that he was emphasizing four principal themes that crop up again and again in our thinking about the practice of psychiatry, and particularly in the education of physicians and psychiatrists. These themes are *1.* human development in its broadest sense, *2.* human learning, especially socially induced learning, *3.* human communication, verbal and nonverbal, and *4.* the social field, particularly the early social field as determinants of the above. The early social field of man is the family, and the family will still turn out to be the most important biological school of man. Yet in our culture the family has abdicated to the expert. We are not without blame in this strange and sad phenomenon—a measure, alike, of both public passivity and professional arrogance. Society has saddled psychiatry with the bills that are Society's rather than psychiatry's; it is time psychiatry returned to the school what is the school's, to the church what is the church's, and to the family what is the family's.

If you think this is a confusing field, you are right. Like the patient said to the psychiatrist, "He who understands the situation is not fully informed."

REFERENCE

1. Rioch, M. J., Elkes, C., and Flint, A. A.: Pilot Project in Training Mental Health Counselors, USPHS Pub #1254, US Dept of Health, Education, and Welfare, Washington, DC, 1965.

3

Social Class and Individual Development *

LEON EISENBERG, MD

*Professor of Child Psychiatry, The Johns Hopkins University
School of Medicine, Baltimore*

*Individual development is an emergent from the interaction
between the biologic potentialities of the infant and the physical
and social particularities of its immediate environment. The
ultimate attainments of a given individual are thus highly dependent on the social field that determines the nutrition, health
care, cognitive stimuli, class membership and interpersonal
atmosphere that can accelerate or impede self-realization.*

*Studies of child development provide convincing evidence that
human malfunction results in large part from society's failure
to employ its resources equitably for human betterment. A firm
commitment to invest in human renewal, based on what we now
know even as we undertake to learn more, can produce intellectual and emotional gains in the coming generation.*

DEVELOPMENTAL PHENOMENA SURROUND US at every turn. We
ourselves are born, grow, decline, die. Nations are formed, achieve
dominion, ultimately survive only in history. Ideas, too, are born,
flourish, and recede when their time is past. An understanding of
events in the real world must begin with an understanding of the
process of change as it occurs in the course of development.

And yet this has been the doctrine of the few rather than of the
many. For every philosopher who has told us that all is flux, another has admonished us that the appearance of change is but a
delusion, that we are tricked by our unreliable senses. Or if change

* Studies reported in this chapter have been supported by funds from the
National Institute of Mental Health (MH-02583), the Grant Foundation of
New York City, and the Office of Economic Opportunity (#510).

is admitted, it is motion in a circle that comes ever back to its beginning.

I.

The doctrine of development has been long in gestation. Even today, when advocated, it is advocated only in the sense that the mature organism is seen as the ultimate toward which the past has progressed and not as the point from which the future shall depart. That is, the end at which the past arrives is taken as the motive force behind the apparent change. But if that is the case, then the idea of the end was present from the beginning; only the material forms, trivial and secondary, have changed, not the essence, the Platonic ideal, which has remained unaltered, eternal.

This may seem an oddly philosophical introduction to a clinical presentation. But, in my view, our conceptual premises, rarely made explicit, result in a static view of man, in which the explanatory power of the idea of development has been vitiated by reducing it to an "unfolding" of what was present from the first. Permit me to elaborate this thesis by contrasting two doctrines of development that, though antique in their origins, have vigorous contemporary proponents.

The first, the doctrine of preformationism, is best exemplified in a charming passage from the Roman poet Seneca: "In the seed are enclosed all the parts of the body of the man that shall be formed. The infant that is borne in his mother's wombe hath the rootes of the beard and hair that he shall weare one day. In this little masse likewise are all the lineaments of the bodie and all that which Posterity shall discover in him." So compelling was this idea that, 1,500 years later, the first microscopists persuaded themselves that they could see an homunculus in the head of the sperm. It had to be there; in consequence, they saw it there.

We do the same when we "account for" behavioral differences in the disadvantaged by inferring an hereditary deficiency, something lacking from the first, or when we "explain" the apparent ubiquity of aggressive behavior by inferring the existence of an aggressive instinct, as Freud did when he wrote: "The very emphasis of the commandment: Thou shalt not kill, makes it certain that we are descended from an endlessly long chain of generations of murderers, whose love of murder was in their blood as it is perhaps also in our own. . . . the man of prehistoric times lives on, unchanged, in our unconscious . . . the primitive psyche is in the strictest sense indestructible. . . ." [1] The relevance of this quotation to our present theme is independent of the position that we take on the role of aggression in human behavior. I cite it because it includes two characteristic psychoanalytic concepts: one, the invocation of an instinct, an inborn drive, to explain behavior; two, the hypothesis that a part of the psychic structure, the unconscious, is impervious to change.

Contrast predeterminism with the doctrine of epigenesis, which we owe to Aristotle. Having studied chick embryos, as his contemporaries had, but placing more reliance than they on observation unconstrained by theory, he could not accept the conventional view that all parts of the embryo were present from the first, but simply were invisible to the eye. He argued that this could not be the case, since parts that were ultimately to be larger (such as the lung) appeared later in development than those that were smaller (such as the heart). In attempting to account for this mystery, he concluded: "It is possible then that A should move B and B should move C; that, in fact, the case should be the same as with the automatic machines shown as curiosities. For the parts of such machine while at rest have the potentiality of motion in them and when any external force puts the first of them into motion, immediately the next is moved in actuality. . . . plainly, then, while there is something which makes the parts, this does not exist as a definite object, nor does it exist in the semen at the first as a complete part. . . ." For all the limitations inherent in the analogy to a self-contained clock-work mechanism, this can be taken as the first statement of the modern doctrine of development: successive stage-related differentiations resulting in new structures and new functions. That is, C_0 (the constituents of the conceptus) produces C_1, which in the presence of S_1 and E_1 (substrate and energy source) produces C_2, which in the presence of S_2 and E_2 produces C_3, and so on.

If for so long investigators have failed to discern the dependence of the developmental process on interchange with the environment, this can be attributed in part to the remarkable workings of the evolutionary mechanism. Over eons of time, individual development has been attuned with extraordinary sensitivity to the predictably occurring regularities of the average environment. It would indeed have been inefficient to build into the genetic code biochemical or behavioral sequences that can be supplied or stimulated from without. Thus, man cannot manufacture the amino acids termed "essential," though he could have (microorganisms do); he relies upon biotic foodstuffs for the ingredients he cannot synthesize. It is only in the presence of dietary deficiency that we detect his vulnerabilities. In similar fashion, the genetically determined complexities of the primate visual system, though functional at birth, lose their *anatomical* integrity in the absence of light stimuli.[2] It is only when the experimentalist is ingenious enough to test limiting conditions that we become aware that what seems automatic (or, if you will, instinctive) is dependent on biological or psychological inputs.

A disclaimer may be necessary here. I am not suggesting that heredity is irrelevant. No environment will make a mouse into a cat or a monkey into a man. But neither mouse nor cat nor monkey nor man will develop from the egg into the adult of its species without a favorable environment. As we ascend from mouse to man, the variability in ultimate attainment that can be accounted for by variability in environment increases many fold. The strategy of evolution has been one of ever greater reliance on learned as opposed to reflexive behavior. Accompanying this trend has been a shift in the ratio of extrauterine to intrauterine brain growth. The great apes double their brain size from birth to maturity; man quadruples his. That is to say, three quarters of human brain growth occurs postnatally; is it not likely that anatomic structure itself is shaped in an important way by experience? For our exquisite adaptability, we pay a heavy price in our vulnerability during infancy to misshaping and stunting by social misfortune; but, at the gamble of this hazard, we attain our potential for creativity and generosity.

II.

With this much for introduction, we may sketch in some influences of social class on individual development. Manifestly, this is a topic for a book, not a chapter. I shall limit myself to strategic examples. My intent is to convey the implications of a developmental view for therapeutic intervention. We deal here, not with academic issues of concern only to specialists and philosophers, but rather with urgent matters that now exercise political leaders and ordinary citizens abroad as well as here.[3] We are but two years removed from a presidential election in which a leading candidate, apparently speaking for some 25 million American voters, opined that poverty is the result of the stupidity or indolence of the poor.

To illustrate the consequences of a developmental vs. a static viewpoint, I shall consider briefly three issues imbedded in the complex interaction between social class and individual development: *1.* nutrition, disease and brain development, *2.* cognitive stimulation and intellectual performance, and *3.* life experience and self-concept.

Nutrition, Disease, and Brain Development

In this age of the common man, the great society and the war against poverty, tens of millions of children throughout the world suffer from chronic protein-calorie malnutrition. For these children, the superimposition of an episode of infection is sufficient to precipitate the syndrome of kwashiorkor, the behavioral manifestations of which include apathy and developmental retardation.[4] The infectious episodes are more likely to occur in the malnourished and hence immunologically vulnerable child and are consequent upon rudimentary and even perverse sanitary practices. Folk medical traditions may lead to "treatment" by further restriction of food intake, thus enhancing the malnutrition. Or ill-advised medical treatment, by overly ambitious attempts at rapid correction of electrolyte imbalance or by the use of antibiotics that precipitate vitamin deficiencies through altering the intestinal flora, may increase the neurologic sequelae. The distribution of illness episodes is related to age of child, both as age reflects differences in immunologic responsiveness and as it is an index of the feeding practices. Repeated and severe episodes are associated with a marked stunting in ultimate height attainment. The youngsters so victimized are stigmatized for life by their short stature. When children in a Guatemalan village were tested for intersensory integration, those in the lowest quartile for height were significantly inferior in performance to those in the highest quartile. Longitudinal studies of individual development will be necessary to confirm the hypothesis that brain development as well as physical growth is impaired by malnutrition, but the evidence is compelling enough to warrant a major campaign for preventive intervention.[5]

I have not attempted to detail the massive evidence on this

question. I have given a telegraphic account stressing the inter-relationships between *diet* (a function of the availability of food as well as of cultural practices and eating habits), *infection* (in turn dependent on housing, sanitation and health information), *treatment methods* (whether "superstitious" or "modern"), and *level of brain development* (a function of the interaction between genetic and environmental factors), all of which interact to influence ultimate intellectual status. The final common pathways are biologic; but the intervening links in the chain are social. They include the beliefs of people, the social structure of the community that results in differential access to food and medical care, and child rearing practices, such as age of weaning and feeding patterns, that influence the frequency of diarrhea, the likelihood of malnutrition, and so on.

Fortunately, only a minority of American children are at this extreme risk. It is not yet clear whether lesser degrees of dietary deprivation may result in less dramatic though still detectable effects on intellectual development. It seems not unreasonable to suppose that there may be a continuum. Nor would I argue that the children in Guatemala show mental retardation solely because of protein deficiency; they also suffer from cognitive malnutrition. Indeed, it is not unlikely that the two factors interact to produce a more devastating result than either would alone.[6]

But in this country, there is compelling evidence of an association between the complications of pregnancy and parturition and the social class of the mother. The mothers at risk are the poor, the Negro, the unmarried, and those at both extremes of the age distribution. These obstetrical complications—eclampsia, infection, prematurity and so on—are in turn associated with a higher risk for brain damage among the surviving offspring.[7] The extent to which these problems occur among the privileged is a measure of our remaining ignorance of their causes; their greater frequency among the underprivileged is a measure of our failure to apply what we know.

The consequences of this cycle of pregnancy complications, malnutrition, infection, and defects in brain growth are enormous for world history. The available evidence indicates that the underdeveloped nations of the world and the underdeveloped areas of the developed nations will be handicapped, not only in this epoch by infantile mortality and morbidity, but in the coming generation of young adults impaired in their capacities by the misfortunes suffered in childhood. We deal here not with a natural catastrophe or medical problem that waits on future research. We know what needs to be done, we have the means to do it, we lack only the commitment to insure that no child starves and that no child is denied the best medical care.[8]

Cognitive Stimulation and Intellectual Development

But if the brain is dependent for its growth on biologic alimentation, the mind is no less dependent upon what Piaget had the foresight to call psychological alimentation. His brilliant clinical observations on his own children documented the successive stages in intellectual development, each stage building on prior mental structures and each transformed as it accommodates to novel experience by developing more inclusive and hence more powerful cognitive operations. Unconcerned with individual differences, Piaget was led to the conception of an invariant age-related sequence in intellectual development as maturation proceeded. But his emphasis on development as occurring through the accommodation of mental structures to new experiences that force change provides the principal basic to an understanding of class-related differences in intellectual function.[9]

The phenomenon that we are concerned to understand is the profusely documented test inferiority of children and adolescents of the lowest social class. Whatever index of intellectual performance we choose—intelligence quotient, creativity, academic achievement, or more simply pass-fail records and school dropouts—a highly significant relationship to social class can be demonstrated. Rather than review the literature, I shall illustrate the point with some data that we have gathered and analyzed.[10] Table 1 indicates the reading scores for sixth-grade children in a representative American city, for its adjacent county ("suburbia"), for its private schools (independent) and for a nearby "bedroom" county of

TABLE 1. *Sixth-grade Reading Levels by School System*

| SCHOOL SYSTEM | TEST | % RETARDED | | % ADVANCED |
		> 2 yrs.	> 1 yr.	> 2 yrs.
Metropolis	Stanford	28	57	9
Commuter County	California	15	35	8
Suburbia	Iowa	3	19	34
Independent	Stanford	0	1	82

mixed rural and commuter residents. The enormous differences require no commentary! Income distributions for these groups would show similar skewing. As to IQ differences, in a current study of children of middle and low social class, we obtained a mean Wechsler IQ of 111 for the middle and 90 for the low, a difference of 21 points, highly significant in a study population of almost 300 children.

The question remains: Why these enormous differences? Three conflicting hypotheses have their current advocates. The first ascribes the findings to innate, that is inherited, differences in intellectual potential. Membership in lower social class groups is regarded as a consequence of drift of the less able into the marginal segments of society and the perpetuation of class inequalities by assortative mating of individuals with subnormal biologic endowment. This belief has the comforting corollary that we who hold membership in the upper classes are where we are because of our merit in this best of all possible worlds. The similarity of this belief to the theological doctrine of predeterminism, the conceptual parallel of the biologic belief in preformationism, should not require further comment.

A second, and currently somewhat more fashionable view, begins with the assertion that although the children may not have differed significantly at the outset (at least if one removes the fraction with brain defects), the cumulative consequences of early deprivation have resulted in irreparable stunting of intellectual function. According to the advocates of this view, the greatest part of the externally modifiable variance in intelligence occurs during the first five years of life. This doctrine of early deprivation differs from the doctrine of hereditary deficit in suggesting that early intervention may be effective in overcoming the inequality, but has similar consequences for public educational policy in implying the futility of remedial measures within the school period.

The third, the one that flows from a developmental viewpoint, regards the manifest differences in test scores a differences in *behavior* and refuses to invoke a construct such as "innate intelligence" to account for this difference, for what is termed "innate" intelligence is unmeasurable. All we can measure—and what in fact we do measure—is performance, not potential. Performance is profoundly altered by learning, not only learning of the specific task but the acquisition of learning sets—that is, modes of approach to problems of a similar class. Indeed, if it is potential that one wishes to study, it can be studied in a meaningful fashion only by providing optimal learning opportunities and then recording the differential responsiveness of individual children. To infer intelligence from performance without controlling for environmental variance would be the same as studying the genetics of proficiency in French without taking into account the language spoken by the child's parents. This third position argues that the possibilities for remediation exist at all ages, though they may be more effective at some than at others. Its action implications call for school enrichment early, continuing *and* late. The existence of individual differences is not denied, but they are regarded as irrelevant to social class; all studies have agreed in finding distributions of performance with overlap between all social classes, with quite bright and quite dull youngsters found in each.

What evidence can be summoned to decide between these competing theories? I shall rely on illustrative examples from our own work with brief reference to other studies.

In the summer of 1965, about 500 children were enrolled in the Baltimore Head Start Project for preschool enrichment of five-year-old slum dwellers. Half of them came from families with annual incomes of less than $3,000, 90% from families with incomes of less than $5,000. Data on parents' education and occupation confirmed the marginal status of these families. Our original design had called for testing of registered but unenrolled children as a control group at the start of the program, but no such group was available. Perforce, our control comparison was limited to an after-test contrasting children from the same neighborhoods and the same classrooms in kindergarten in September, with and without the summer experience.

TABLE 2. *PPVT Raw Scores*

	CONTROL	HEADSTART			STAND. SAMPLE
		H_1	H_2	H_3	
Mean	33.65	32.63	36.83	39.74	50.22
S.D.	11.70	12.33	10.82	11.34	8.17
Number	*402*	*424*	*413*	*402*	*133*

Table 2 shows the mean raw scores on the Peabody Picture Vocabulary Test (PPVT) for the Head Start children on enrollment in late June, on completion of the program in early August, and on entering kindergarten in mid-September at the time the controls were tested. The record is one of progressive gains; the changes are highly significant and far exceed those ascribable to the ten-week gain in age. Head Start pretest (H_1) and control hardly differ, but the Head Start group is superior at better than the .001 level at the second (H_2) and third (H_3) testings, though it is still inferior to the standardization sample in the Peabody manual.

The flaw in our design (the lack of time-locked testing of the controls) raises the question whether test practice can account for the differences. Data from successive testing of deprived children, made available to us by Professor Susan Gray, shows no such effect on successive testing as do other published studies; the gains can be ascribed to the preschool program. Similar results were obtained on 400 Head Start and 400 control children with the Draw-A-Person test employed as a measure of intellectual maturation. We have confirmatory evidence from more intensive studies on control and Head Start subsamples tested by the Binet, by the Columbia Mental Maturity Scale, and by special perceptual tests. Furthermore, data just analyzed on 80 matched pairs of control and Head Start children retested after eight months of kindergarten demonstrate continuing, though less marked, superiority of the Head Start group.[11]

That these benefits, documented for the short run and stemming from brief periods of intervention, can in fact lead to enduring benefit in intellectual performance *if backed by continuing enrichment* (and I call attention to this conditional clause) has been shown by Gray over a two-year follow-up period [12] and by Skeels in a 30-year follow-up.[13]

But what of intervention later? In a current study of concept induction, Dr. Sonia Osler's results indicate significant increases in performance following training for eight- as well as five-year-old children. Moreover, in clinical studies of stimulant drug treatment for children with hyperkinetic behavior disorders, ten years in mean age, we have obtained highly significant increases in Porteus IQ in the drug as opposed to the placebo group, with the greatest gains registered among the children initially in the defective range on Wechsler Intelligence testing.[14] It is a matter of definition whether one interprets this finding to indicate that the treatment "improved" intelligence, or whether it merely permitted the children, by enhanced attention and impulse control, to "demonstrate" the intelligence that they had from the first. The essential point of concern here is that intelligence test measures, conventionally employed for class grouping and for prediction of achievement, can be modified by appropriate psychological and pharmacological intervention, a view divergent from the traditional faith in the IQ as a measure of a fundamental characteristic of the child.

To summarize, intellectual development requires appropriate cognitive stimulation at all stages of the life cycle. Present information argues that deficiencies detected in the socially disadvantaged are most parsimoniously ascribed to exogenous rather than endogenous factors, at least until the best program of social and educational enrichment that we can design has failed to produce the anticipated benefit. Only then can the suggestion of intrinsic deficit be logically maintained.

Life Experience and Self-Concept

When we turn to the last of the three issues, the relationship between the envelope of life experience and the self-concept of the individual, I must rely on clinical observation and inference. This is an honorable enterprise in medicine; such preliminary endeavors permit the formulation of testable hypotheses.

Self-concept, the individual's inner view of himself vis-a-vis the world of others, is a large and inclusive domain. I shall limit my comments to one area: the sense of potency—that is, the extent to which the individual views himself as captain of his fate and as capable of attaining success through his own efforts. Obviously, no one but a fool or a megalomaniac thinks that he can bring his ship safely to shore whatever storms ensue; but the man whom we take to be well-integrated sees himself as an active participant in the determination of his future and has a conviction of competence in managing his affairs, if extraordinary circumstances be excluded.

There's the rub; we confront at once crucial differences in class-determined experience: the kinds of circumstances that are ordinary and extraordinary. You and I, occupying roles of high prestige ascription, the possessors of valued skills, know, or ought to know, that we will be rewarded for our work and that we have the option of shifting positions in pursuing the dictates of personal interest. That all of us may *not* have this underlying confidence merely demonstrates that idiosyncratic as well as class-related life experiences join in shaping personality, but that is another story.

Now, the obverse of the coin of potency is belief in a world of ordered events and predictable consequences. It is simple enough to learn that apples fall from trees, if apples always fall, and to generalize lawful relations between height of fall, velocity and acceleration. But if apples sometimes fell and sometimes rose in random fashion, no such generalization would be possible, and the task of picking them would be frustrating and perhaps beyond accomplishment. We would then be led to envoke hypotheses of malign spirits and would likely spend our time propitiating them by magic rituals—under the circumstances as useful a device as any.

Apples do fall and none of us fails to learn that they do. But the relationship between personal effort and social reward does not necessarily follow any such simple law of social gravitation; the lower one descends in the social order, the more the apparent randomness in the distribution of antecedents and consequents. For the child of the lowest social class—of the disorganized, unemployable, multiple problem family—the world is almost chaotic. The ordinary regularities of time and place in family life—mealtimes, hours of awakening and going to sleep, places for things to be, familiar actors in the family drama—shift, change, and dance about. In consequence, the developmental acquisition of the concepts of space, time and person is retarded and distorted.[15] Blurred and unstable axes in these fundamentals of mental geometry obscure the task of discerning the relationship between what one does and what follows after.

These strictures, mind you, apply to life at home and to negotiating the middle-class world. Out in the alleys of the slum, the rules are clear and the child learns fast; the price of ignorance is too high to pay. But what he learns on the streets has little currency in the structure of school and industry. His home has failed him in its fundamental task of providing cognitive maps of the middle-class social terrain where the rewards of or society are to be found.

When a harrassed and overburdened mother sometimes says *yes,* sometimes *no,* more often ignores what is asked or told, but suddenly acts on the impulse of her own inner needs rather than responding in contigent fashion to what the child has said or done, he cannot learn to predict what his acts will bring and has difficulty discerning the relevance of his own behavior to his fate. His position is akin to Ruth Benedict's Dobu Islander who attributes success or failure to the benign or malignant motivation of his neighbor. How can a parent create for her child a belief in the efficacy of personal effort as a determinant of personal fortune, when skin color if she's black, or automation if she's unskilled, or the frequency of illness if she's poor, all issues beyond personal control, destroy the job, the savings, the very dreams of the hardest working and the most diligent?

How can a conviction of personal competence be sustained in a child whose impoverished language, whose unfamiliarity with formal learning situations, whose concrete and situation-bound repertoire of responses all conjoin to ensure failure in a school that expects him to arrive already trained and that rejects as inappropriate the behaviors he has had to acquire for survival on the streets? School becomes the place where he discovers what he cannot do rather than being taught to do. Unless he walls off the school hours as irrelevant to real life, he acquires an abiding sense of incompetence, because, as he sees it, he has tried and failed. Having stopped trying, he continues to fail; he has acquired his life role, that of failure. Dr. Gilbert Schiffman, in a study of 80 slow learners, found that despite intelligence at least in the low normal range, these children were perceived by their teachers *and* their parents as dullards; need it surprise us that four-fifths of these children, on being asked to rate themselves in intelligence, described themselves as dull or stupid?

However, let me emphasize that the basic issue is *not* one of parental "reassurance" or saccharine compliments from the teacher for a child who performs poorly. A sense of potency can be derived only from the experience of mastery: seeing one's self, hearing one's self, feeling one's self *succeed*. And to accomplish that, for a child who enters school with proficiency in academically dystonic behavior and deficits in the fundamental psychological attributes antecedent to academic learning, requires understanding the child's cognitive profile, building on the skills he brings with him, and working seriously at the challenge of shifting his set so that he works at developing competence. This will not be done—it has not been done—in classes of 40 or 50, by teachers prepared only for middle-class children, in schools that are architectural monstrosities. Indeed, if one were asked to define the mental health responsibilities of public schools, the most meaningful reply would be: the enabling of children to learn, to acquire skills, to experience mastery and, on that basis, to develop a sense of potency.

III.

The process of development, of the brain and of the mind, is a resultant of the interaction between organism and environment. In that process, a sequential series of transformations occurs, in the course of which new structures and functions appear and prior structures and functions are fundamentally altered in their properties. There can be no return to what *was,* though remnants of what *was* are incorporated in what *is,* and what *is* provides the building blocks for what *will be.* Psychic development cannot be understood on the basis of Freud's attractive but misleading simile [16]: "Psychic evolution shows a peculiarity which is not found in any other process of development. When a town becomes a city or a child grows into a man, town and child disappear in the city and in the man. . . . It is different in the case of psychic evolution . . . every previous stage of development is preserved next to the following one from which it has evolved . . . the primitive psyche is in the strictest sense indestructible. . . ." On the contrary, each previous stage of psychic evolution undergoes transmutation in the crucible of experience to become a more inclusive, a more adaptive structure.

The preservation of the very integrity of the brain, not to mention the conditions necessary for its maturation, is intimately dependent on the supply of foodstuffs and stimuli from the environment. The growth of human cognitive function, an achievement that parallels the prolongation of the immaturity of the human infant, occurs only in a nurturing and stimulating interpersonal context. The elaboration of the sense of self, and in particular the acquisition of a sense of individual potency, builds on the experience of success in mastering life's demands.

Developmental theory has important implications for public policy, especially for those of us whose business is the remediation of pathology in behavior. We must become articulate advocates for those whose malfunction is the morally intolerable consequence of society's failure to employ its resources equitably for human betterment. I would remind you of the concluding words of Sir Charles P. Snow's address on "The Moral Un-Neutrality of Science." [17]

> All this we know. It throws upon scientists a direct and personal responsibility. It is not enough to say that scientists have

a responsibility as citizens. They have a much greater one than that, and one different in kind. For scientists have a moral imperative to say what they know. It is going to make them unpopular in their own nationstates. It may do worse than make them unpopular. That doesn't matter. Or at least, it does matter to you and me, but it must not count in the face of the risks. . . .

For scientists know, and again with the certainty of scientific knowledge, that we possess every scientific fact we need to transform the physical life of half the world. And transform it within the span of people now living. I mean, we have all the resources to help half the world live as long as we do and eat enough. All that is missing is the will. . . .

There are going to be challenges to our intelligence and to our moral nature as long as man remains man. After all, a challenge is not, as the word is coming to be used, an excuse for slinking off and doing nothing. A challenge is something to be picked up. . . .

REFERENCES

1. Freud, S.: Reflections on War and Death, trans. by Brill, A. A., and Kuttner, A. B., New York, Moffat, Yard & Company, 1918, pp. 60-61.

2. Wiesel, T. N., and Hubel, D. H.: Effects of visual deprivation on morphology and physiology of cells in the cat's lateral geniculate body. J Neurophysiol 26:978-993, 1963.

3. Eisenberg, L.: Can human emotions be changed? Bull Atomic Scientists, 22:27-31, 1966.

4. Cravioto, J., and Robles, B.: Evolution of adaptive and motor behavior during rehabilitation from kwashiorkor, Amer J Orthopsychiat 35:449, 1965.

5. Cravioto, J., Delicarde, E. R., and Birch, H. G.: Nutrition, growth, and neurointegrative development: an experimental and ecologic study, Pediatrics 38:319-372, 1966.

6. Eisenberg, L.: Behavioral manifestations of cerebral damage in childhood, in Birch, H. G., ed.: Brain Damage in Children, Baltimore, Williams and Wilkins, 1964.

7. Pasamanick, B., and Knobloch, H.: Retrospective studies on the epidemiology of reproductive casualty: old and new, Merrill-Palmer Quart Behav and Develop 12:7-26, 1966.

8. Eisenberg, L.: If not now, when? Amer J Orthopsychiat 32:781-793, 1962.

9. Hunt, J. McV.: Intelligence and Experience, New York, Ronald Press, 1961.

10. Eisenberg, L.: Reading retardation I. Psychiatric and sociologic aspects, Pediatrics 37:352-365, 1966.

11. Waller, D. A., and Conners, C. K.: A follow-up study of intelligence changes in children who participated in project Head Start, unpublished manuscript, 1967.

12. Gray, S. W., and Klaus, R. A.: An experimental preschool program for culturally deprived children, Child Develop *36*:887-898, 1965.

13. Skeels, H. H.: Adult status of children with contrasting early life experiences, Monogr Soc Res Child Develop, Serial #105, *31*:(#3), 1966.

14. Conners, C. K., and Eisenberg, L.: The effects of methylphenidate on symptomatology and learning in disturbed children, Amer J Psychiat *120*:458-463, 1963.

15. Eisenberg, L.: The sins of the fathers, Amer J Orthopsychiat *32*:5-17, 1962.

16. Freud, S.: *Op. cit.*, pp. 30-31.

17. Snow, C. P.: The moral un-neutrality of science, Science *133*:255-259, 1961.

Discussion

EUGENE B. BRODY, MD

Professor and Chairman, Department of Psychiatry, Director, The Psychiatric Institute, University of Maryland School of Medicine, Baltimore

I WOULD DISCUSS the impact of society, culture, and man's unique capacity for complex symbolization in relation to this problem of human development. I shall not fight the battle of heredity, because I consider it a straw man. I shall ignore the impact of perinatal influence and brain damage, because that is already adequately documented, and I shall discuss the matter of social deprivation in a very general sense in language somewhat different from that used by Dr. Eisenberg, a language derived largely from my personal background in psychoanalysis.

It is quite true—I think that we need not document this—that many studies indicate that the conditions associated with growing up in a socially deprived environment increase the likelihood that a child will not perform well on intelligence tests. There are many possible causative factors. These range from the deficit in the input and the complexity of situations, identified by Hebb and Heron about 25 years ago in their pioneering study on isolated animals, to such matters as failure in identity training—through the absence of birthday parties or personal photographs, for example, or through the failure to be addressed regularly by a consistent first name. This is documented by Langner and Michael, and others, in the midtown Manhattan study.

We can note, also, that intelligence should not be considered as a unitary concept any more than social class. For example, the ability to deal in abstractions, and the capacity to handle an immediate threatening or concrete situation are both aspects of intelligence. Is it possible that the premature development of one aspect might occur at the expense of the other? What about the three- or four-year-old boy who learns how to cross a wide traffic-

81

laden street without being hit, or to go into a grocery store, give the clerk a previously specified amount of money, receive the change that he has been told to expect, pick up a quart of milk, cross that big street again and get safely home? What is the cost of this achievement in terms of his ability to reflect, to abstract elements from a variety of situations, and to put them together in a new way? Or to create or possibly even to feel deeply about certain kinds of things?

If the circumstances of life in its most formative and impressionable years require intense and vigilant attention to the details of external reality, what does this do to the balance of ego defenses on the one hand, and the adaptive mechanisms on the other? One might look at the mechanism of denial, for example, following Heinz Hartmann's theory, in two ways. One way, in ego defensive terms, is as a means of shutting out the emotionally disturbing impact of real life, but permitting a more dominant role to pleasurable fantasy, and promoting a more stable intrapsychic equilibrium at the expense of the person's adaptive equilibrium—that is, his reciprocal relationships with his environment. Second, the mechanism of denial can be viewed in the service of a person's adaptive processes—thus, it can be possible for thinking, problem solving or planning for the future to take place with relative, although temporary, freedom from the anxious or the depression-producing pressures of immediate reality. Our own observations suggest rather strongly that the experience of growing up as a member of a deprived and threatened minority increases the likelihood of denial being utilized as a defense rather than in the service of adaptation, often with the assistance of narcotics or alcohol. The pressure on this and related elements of the psychological defense system for anxiety reduction or for facilitating the use of fantasy as a substitute for unacceptable life circumstances seems in fact almost to preclude its adaptive use. I look on this only as one specific instance of what—on the basis of the work of Sibyl Escalona, Erikson, Marianne Kris and others—is probably going to turn out to be a general rule: that very early and intense activation of the psychological defense system, promoting the erection of a protective barrier between the child and sources of overwhelming stimulation, will result in inhibitions or defects in his capacity to symbolize, to learn anything not necessary for immediate survival, to abstract, to be flexible, or to be creative. This fits some of the formulations of the late Ernst Kris, who pointed to the importance of a permeable barrier between what is conscious and what is preconscious, and the capacity to think creatively, or to put the elements of an intellectual puzzle together. And as you recall, Kris referred to the creative process as involving a temporary dipping into the preconscious stream, with an, again temporary, abandonment, in Freud's terms, of real objects. He called this regression in the service of the ego. He and others interested in the same phenomena, such as Kubie, have suggested strongly that the kind of rigid defense system that is built under the pressures of potentially overwhelming anxiety does not permit the temporary relinquishing of reality contact necessary for such momentary regression. You can see that I am approaching the social-class, intellectual-development point of view from a somewhat different angle. This is *not* from the point of view of the quantity or even of the quality, in terms of the content or novelty of experience often subsumed under the heading of enrichment, nor of the positive learning impact of situations to which the child is exposed, but rather of their evocative power in terms of anxiety, in terms of guilt, in terms of perhaps shame or disgust. Claude Brown wrote in *Manchild in the Promised Land* that after sitting three hours on the stairs in front of the Harlem tenement of his childhood, he saw and heard so much that he could have spent eight or 12 hours talking about it, if given a chance.

I think that when we conceptualize the atmosphere of "childhood deprivation" in terms of stimulation or input, the problem really isn't too little but probably too much, of the wrong kind, too early, and perhaps of greatest importance, with no opportunity to talk it out, to work it through with someone on whom the child can be comfortably dependent. I suspect for our deprived children in the United States any impairment in the thinking machine itself is less important in producing impaired intellectual and creative capacity than the defensive rigidities and inhibitions on the one hand and the hypervigilance to certain aspects of external reality on the other, which have been necessary for survival in early life.

If we must think in terms of environmental deficit, what is missing, I believe, is the opportunity for certain types of relationships. Our own studies of deprived boys in Baltimore suggested, for example, a specific socially fostered problem in achieving a satisfactory identification with father figures, because either no fathers were in the home or those who were were remote or brutal.

But it also seemed related to what was pointed out by the late Walter Adams, a Negro psychiatrist from Chicago, and others who were concerned with this matter of potency to which Dr. Eisenberg alluded—that even in their own homes these boys were not able to see their fathers, or for that matter their mothers, as strong or secure upholders of their own rights. And many of us, not uniquely, suspect on the basis of clinical evidence that a satisfactory experience of identifying with a parental figure is a very important prerequisite in the capacity to perform in later relationships, including those with teachers and people who give tests. Our own data suggest that many, perhaps the majority, of socially deprived children receive conflicting messages from their mothers about matters relevant to the development of ambition and achievement. Thus at the verbal level they hear: Your opportunities are as good as anyone's and you should set your sights high; at the nonverbal level: You really haven't got a chance, and anyway, I myself don't know enough about what's going on to help you, and I'm not even sure that I want you to do so much better than I that I lose you. This kind of experience also does something to the child's later capacity to relate to school teachers and to other key figures of the social control system.

Finally, I believe that the lower-class child, especially one who belongs to a socially visible minority, is not just deprived but actively excluded. Cultural exclusion is a term that I have used to refer to the active denial by members of the power-holding majority of the privilege of full participation in the culture of the society to those of the minority. This ultimately means that the excluded man who doesn't share in the value systems of the majority is a victim of certain kinds of cultural discontinuities. He possesses a limited range of cultural symbols to work with, and he knows that the group that sets the standards and the group that controls the institutions is one to which he can never belong. The implications of this situation for the lower-class child and the adolescent have been spelled out elsewhere. I will only note, in concluding, that a deficit in intellectual development or intelligence summarizes and condenses the impact of cultural exclusion on planning for and achieving long-range goals, engaging in collective action for individual gain, abstracting from concrete situations and forming new syntheses, conforming to the wishes of parents or parental substitutes, adhering to a conventional system of morality, and even functioning as a psychotherapeutic patient.

EISENBERG, REPLY

As I UNDERSTAND THE MAIN DRIFT of Dr. Levay's commentary, he raises the following points: that genius appears in the midst of poverty (e.g., Franz Schubert); that wealthy families rarely produce genius; and that in fact I have been beating a dead horse in focusing on the heredity versus environment controversy. I will try to respond to these points seriatim and then go to Dr. Brody's discussion.

I daresay that no one in this audience would voluntarily undergo poverty or recommend deprivation as a therapeutic measure to produce genius. The fact that one can point to a poet, a composer or a scientist who, despite poverty, went on to demonstrate his gifts, tells us nothing about how many other similarly gifted people have been lost to posterity by the degrading effects of an impoverished environment. Thomas Gray's "Elegy Written in a Country Churchyard" said this in a way I cannot improve on.

I trust that the speaker is not really serious when he suggests that the concentration camp may have beneficial effects. It may be true that rare individuals emerged from this cataclysm and still rose to great heights. The first requirement, of course, was survival, and only a pitiful few made that. Follow-up examinations of the survivors of these camps have revealed chronic neurologic and psychiatric sequelae among many of those who lived to return from the inferno.

Furthermore, I am not at all persuaded that genius is a product of poverty. Genius has in fact often emerged from wealth. Darwin came from a successful English family; Erasmus Darwin had anticipated Charles's findings and subsequent Darwins have been distinguished physicists and crystallographers. I cannot cite comparative data on the number of distinguished persons who have come from rich and poor families, but any comparative study would have to take into account the remarkably different denominators in the fractions. Unhappily, always far too many have been poor. I am not suggesting either that an affluent society is necessarily the best. I am not suggesting that money brings happiness, though I would advise this audience that if they have to be unhappy, I would recommend that they be rich. The well-to-do do not automatically acquire mental health or genius, but everything that we do know about the conditions that foster mental growth suggests that nutritional hazards, cognitive understimulation and family breakdown are primarily negative forces.

I specified unequivocally that individual differences in behavior do exist and that some portion of this variance must be attributed to heredity. What I did stress is the absurdity of the notion that in the *conceptus* there is something isomorphic with "intelligence." One can reasonably assume that the fertilized egg must have the biochemical precursors of subsequent talent, but precursors that require a series of complicated transactions with a favorable environment in order to lead to those qualities of behavior that we term intelligence. While perhaps very few would any longer state things baldly in terms of heredity verses environment, there is still an important area of controversy with respect to the extent to which variance in one or the other accounts for the manifest variance in performance. The fact of the matter is that this was an issue in the last Presidential campaign, that it still remains as a shibboleth to belabor the poor.

One hears the comment that the problems in Watts are not the lack of hospitals, or jobs, or the cumulative effects of prejudice, but the people in Watts. When I conveyed to the school administrator from whom I had obtained the data on reading scores my distress at the poor achievement of the children, I was greeted with a rejoinder meant to be reassuring. "After all, Doctor", he said, "these children have lower scores on IQ tests." The fact that IQ tests, like reading scores, reflect the cumulative consequences of learning as well as potential for learning seems to have escaped him. He was prepared to avoid his responsibility for this debacle by deciding that it was the children who had failed, not the schools. I regret to say that the issue of heredity *versus* environment isn't dead, but I am prepared to agree that it should long ago have given up the ghost.

To Doctor Brody, I would apologize for giving him one paper and reading another. Yet I could hardly supply the one I was going to read, because it hadn't been written; and, since I repeat myself, he knew essentially what I would say. As a matter of fact, discussants have an agenda, just as speakers do, and they are rarely confined by the text. I say this to Dr. Brody as one experienced discussant to another.

He and I disagree more than he has acknowledged. It is not

simply a matter of employing different terminology. My approach to the problem of the personality consequences of social class is different from his. There is indeed a problem for the Negro boy in the typical lower-class matriachal family in acquiring a sense of maleness, because males in the home are transient and exhibit characteristics that provide poor models for success in our society. On the other hand, there is reason to believe that, rather than having to reconstruct this absent or missing past, the opportunity for Negro adolescents and Negro men to participate directly in civil rights activities, to challenge and change the social structure that treats them as less than men, can lead to a psychological "revolution" that can make them whole again. Kenneth Clark reported to me some years ago that, in Montgomery, Alabama (where the famous bus strike started the passive resistance movement), the number of law violations for which Negroes were booked (other than civil rights activities) fell precipitously. This suggests that the blind, frustrating, angry rage that leads to anti-social behavior can be channeled into socially effective protest and in this process transmute the individual. Dr. Gary O'Connor and associates studied this question in several Southern cities, and again found an inverse relationship between Negro arrests and the existence of an *active* civil rights movement. I would argue that the possibility for reconstructing psychic structure is never lost, though it would seem reasonable to suppose that intervention may be more readily effective at one age than another.

Dr. Brody is correct in suggesting that the mother who, to an interviewer, responds that she would like her child to be an engineer, really doesn't believe he will ever make it and conveys that message covertly to him. But I would argue that that's not the mother's message but society's message. The message is what mother has learned from her social experience and what she has every reason to believe will be her son's. We're not going to change that mother's message without changing her social experience. Beyond this, the mother who wants her child to be an engineer, and even believes he will make it, has to know how to go about making her child an engineer. She has to know that she will make him an engineer by playing games with him, by reading books to him, by expanding his language training, by exposing him to cultural experiences, by giving him a sense of confidence in his own abilities, and so on. This is something that the ill-educated, harrassed, overwhelmed Negro mother by and large does not understand and does not have the time to attempt even when she does understand it.

Professor Robert Hess, of the University of Chicago, brought mothers into the University laboratories, gave them a simple concept problem and taught them how to solve it if they couldn't solve it on their own. Then the mother brought her three-year-old child into the laboratory with the task of teaching the child to solve the problem. The class differences were striking. In general, the lower-class mother employed relatively little verbalization and made little effort to state the abstract principle, but rather depended on direct visual demonstrations. Another story may illustrate the point. Sarah Smilansky, in an unpublished paper, described a study of families of recent immigrants to Israel. Families with four-year-old children were chosen for the investigation. She went into the child's home and there gave him a simple paper-and-pencil test. She went into two types of homes: those of European immigrants and those from Arabic countries, where the Jews had lived under medieval conditions. There were, of course, initial differences between the groups, but the salient point here is that when she returned to the same homes for a second series of test studies, she observed that in the European home it was a common experience to be greeted by a mother who said: "You know, Rachel didn't do very well on that test last time you were here. I want you to try her at it again." She found that the mother had spent the time in between practicing with Rachel, so that she would pass this "college entrance examination" at the age of four. This never, or rarely, happened in the home of the Arabic immigrant. This is the beginning of what we observe in the end as a profound difference in intellectual orientation and attainment.

4

Suggestion and Hypnosis

G. Wilson Shaffer, PhD

*Professor of Psychology and Dean of the Faculty, The Johns
Hopkins University, Baltimore, Past President,
Maryland Psychological Association*

*Seeking to develop a satisfactory theory of hypnosis, all types of
psychologists, from brass-instrument to psychoanalytic, have attained a number of understandings but no satisfactory theory.
Because the hypnotic state must be initiated in the waking state,
attention is finally focused on the overlapping of waking suggestion and the hypnotic state.*

*An experiment has been designed to measure susceptibility to
suggestion and its relation to hypnotizability. Five groups of subjects were given tests of suggestibility by a single investigator,
and after the results were tabulated, hypnosis was attempted
with a sample of the group tested. A second experiment, differing
from the first only by the use of three investigators instead of one,
provides different conclusions regarding suggestibility and
hypnosis.*

THE HISTORY OF PSYCHOLOGY reveals a large number of efforts to
develop a satisfactory theory of hypnosis. Representatives of all
types of psychological thought, from the brass-instrument psychologist to the psychoanalyst, have participated in the theorizing.
As a result, we have attained new understandings, but we have no
satisfactory theory of hypnosis.

The attempts to link hypnosis with sleep have been largely unsatisfactory. Most of the experimental work indicates that the
physiologic responses of the hypnotized subject are more like those
of the waking than of the sleep state. The later efforts of Pavlov [1]
to explain hypnosis as partial sleep have been effectively criticized
by Hull.[2] Confusion still exists, however, as a result of experiments by Darrow and others,[3] in which hypnosis is described as
like light sleep and unlike both deep sleep and the waking state.

The dissociation theory, historically related to the theories of Janet and Prince, although for a long time very popular, has been severely criticized by White and Shevach,[4] and while the theory sheds some light on hypnosis, it is far from complete. Hull's elaboration of James's ideomotor theory into a conditioned response theory, and Welch's [5] attempt to explain hypnosis in terms of abstract conditioning have contributed to the understanding of hypnosis, but fall far short of a satisfactory theory.

The psychoanalytic theories, although stemming from Freud, were best presented by Ferenczi, who saw hypnosis as an evocation of the infantile erotic masochistic relationships toward the parents. Little experimental evidence has been presented to substantiate the theory. Kubie and Margolin [6] later presented an analytic model of hypnosis involving three phases analogous to a natural process of development. Evidence has not been presented to support the position.

White's [7] theory of hypnosis as goal-directed behavior in an altered state of the person and Sarbin's [8] efforts to understand hypnosis as role-taking behavior are examples of motivational theories that have enriched the field but fail to provide a theory. That the subject is motivated to act as the hypnotist wants him to act none denies, but the "altered state" of the person is left as a mystery.

West [9] has taken the position that this altered state of the person may finally be understood by giving attention to the way that humans deal with information—that is, how the brain scans, screens and stores information to make it useful. He has recognized that many of the theories of ego function have given attention to the scanning and screening of information in conceptual terms, but points out that only recently has attention been centered on the physiology of the relationship between the reticular system and the sensory pathways to indicate that the reticular system underwrites the whole process of conscious awareness. The question that remains is how the brain can scan the information that it receives and how it can blot out certain kinds of information. West has called attention to a classical experiment—a cat and mouse game. The cat lies in his cage listening to a clock going tic, tic, tic, and every time that the tic comes a little electrode on the cat's head goes blip, blip, blip, showing that the signals are getting through. Then the mouse is presented. The cat concentrates his attention on the mouse. The tics continue, but the blips disappear. We are left with the necessity of explaining the process by means of which this information is screened out.

More than the reticular activity system must be involved. In hypnosis, an unusual degree of concentration must take place, and more and more information must be screened out. The number of working channels must be decreased as the subject narrows his field of attention. Reality testing in the ordinary sense is not going on, since the information required for reality testing is screened out. If the hypnotist tells the subject he is five years old, he accepts this as reality information and acts accordingly. He does not ask himself, "How come, if I'm five years old, I have this full beard?"

Arnold [10] has attempted to trace the circuits that mediate the sequence from perception to emotion and action, on the basis of recent neurophysiologic research. She takes the position that we know that perception is mediated by neural impulses from the receptor organs to the sensory cortex, and that something perceived will lead to action if the excitation is relayed from the sensory to the motor cortex. The estimate that something is good is viewed as being dependent on a neural connection—from the sensory thalamic and cortical areas to the medial thalamus and the limbic cortex—thus accounting for attention and concentration. The action tendency that follows is seen to be mediated by a connection from the limbic cortex to the hippocampal rudiment and hippocampus, which transforms impulses from sensory and limbic areas into motor impulses—that is, impulses that connect with the midbrain, cerebellum, ventral thalamus and hypothalamus, and finally activate the motor cortex.

Similarly, she has attempted to trace memory and imagination circuits. The induction of hypnosis is consequently seen as eventually excluding all spontaneous action impulses. Muscular relaxation occurs as a result of a deliberate inhibition of action that is accompanied by slow frequency conduction in the action circuit. Cortical activity is thus reduced enough to make external stimuli less intrusive and therefore disregarded. So long as the subject pays attention to the hypnotizer, only one avenue of stimulation remains open: whatever the hypnotist commands is appraised as good to do and so controls memory, imagination and action circuits, and the possibility of distraction is eliminated.

Almost all theoretical efforts to understand the induction of the hypnotic state have been concerned, in one way and another, with the suppressing of spontaneous action impulses and the creation of a state in which the spontaneous appraisal of the environment or of one's actions is prevented. What Arnold has attempted to do is to describe the neurophysiologic pathways involved in this process. What is left as a mystery is why this process should take place with the simplicity of commands used in the induction of hypnosis.

In the absence of any satisfactory theory of hypnosis, it may be profitable to review the relationship between waking suggestibility and hypnosis. Any discussion of hypnosis must lead to a certain amount of overlapping with the topic of waking suggestion, since the hypnotic state is initiated in the waking state. The individual who has not been hypnotized must be led first to respond in the waking state. The distinction between waking suggestions and hypnotic suggestions may for the most part be artificial, since all suggestions are administered in the waking state—otherwise the subject in general would not respond to them.

Much of the confusion results from a failure to attend the extent to which human behavior may be influenced by waking suggestion. The seemingly impossible tasks performed by hypnotic subjects are magnified in the minds of onlookers, since they do not know the capabilities of the unhypnotized individual in making the same performances. There is an abundance of evidence in medicine, law and advertising of the dramatic influence of waking suggestion on behavior. Dorcus and Shaffer [11] have reported on the results of both direct and indirect suggestions by way of indicating that the phenomena produced are comparable to those produced under hypnosis. There have been many studies of suggestibility, but most of them have been done with regard to differences in susceptibility in terms of age or sex, or for a distinction between those who may be referred to as being generally suggestible.

A great variety of tests have been used to measure suggestibility. Murphy [12] has presented an excellent summary of the results of tests of the illusions of size-weight, movement, smell and warmth. Triplett,[13] Small [14] and Guidi [15] have reported studies in children that are in agreement with Gilbert,[16] who reported that suggestibility increased up to about the age of nine and decreased from then on. Most of this work indicates that children are suggestible, probably more suggestible than adults, but caution must be used when making inferences from a specific type of suggestibility to general suggestibility.

Warner Brown's [17] studies of sex differences in suggestibility are probably the most carefully controlled tests in this field. Although most of his tests were similar to those regularly used, a few of them were similar, in some respects, to prestige suggestions. These were based on the principle that if a subject is told what the usual judgment made by others is, or what factors in a situation tend to make for error, he will modify his judgment to conform to the stated average or to compensate for the error factors. The results in general tend to show that women are more suggestible than men. Most investigators have tended to refer to suggestibility as a unit trait, despite the fact that intercorrelations of the tests yield, on the whole, low positive results.

The experimental evidence for the relationship of suggestibility to hypnosis is confusing. Hull [18] has concluded that a number of prestige tests in the waking state are diagnostic of whether the subject is susceptible to hypnosis. The response to suggested arm movement and postural change has been correlated with rate of lid closure and the production of other hypnotic phenomena. On the contrary, the frequency distribution curves of response to waking suggestions of hand levitation, of electric shock, and of a swinging pendulum are "u" shaped curves and do not correspond to the frequency distributions found for responses in hypnosis, which in some cases are linear. Some of the evidence indicates that susceptibility to various forms of nonprestige suggestions is not equal or uniform. Other evidence indicates that prestige suggestions of various types show a high degree of intercorrelation and also correlate with susceptibility to hypnosis. The conclusions are based on data obtained from dissimilar groups of people, techniques, and hypnotists, and consequently leave questions that cannot be answered from the data at hand.

I have attempted an experiment designed to measure susceptibility to suggestion and its relation to hypnotizability. The subjects were divided into five groups, each consisting of 25 subjects: Group 1 of mental patients, Group 2 of physicians and professors, Group 3 of nurses, Group 4 of business executives, and Group 5 of college students. All were given three tests:

TEST I: LENGTHS OF LINES

Across a strip of white paper, 20 parallel straight black lines are drawn 2 cm apart. Each of the first four lines are progressively longer than the line preceding it; all the other lines are the same length. The sheet bearing the lines is placed around a kymograph drum, which lies horizontally on a stand and can be revolved freely by hand. A shield is placed close to and in front of the drum to shield the paper from the subject. An aperture is cut in the shield, so that when the drum is revolved, one line at a time may be exposed to the subject. The subject is seated at a table and has before him a sheet of cross-section paper ruled in millimeter squares.

The instructions are: "I want to test your judgment of the lengths of lines. I will show you a succession of lines. I want you to take one look at the line, judge the length of this line and record your judgment by putting a dot the distance from the left-hand margin of the paper that you think the line is long. When that is done, I will show you the second line, then the third and so on. Make the marks for the second line below the first, the third on the next line, and so on."

TEST II: LENGTHS OF LINES

Test 2 was similar to Test 1, except that the lines shown begin with number 5, and consequently all of the lines shown are of equal length. The instructions to the subjects are similar to those of the first experiment with the following exception. When the experimenter shows the first line, he says, "Here is the first one," when he shows the second line, he says, "Here is a longer one," and when he shows the third line, he says, "Here is a shorter one." He continues to use these remarks alternately as he exposes each line.

TEST III: ILLUSION OF WARMTH

The apparatus consisted of a wooden box, open at the end facing the experimenter and provided on the top with porcelain sockets for four electric lights, wired in multiple and with a snap switch by which the current could be turned on or off. The wiring is purposely left visible, and leads conspicuously to a coil of German silver wire, which is wound, without covering, about a flat piece of hard rubber. This resistance coil is fastened to the front of the box, so that it may be easily reached by the subject without exposing his fingers to the warmth of the lamps on the top of the box. A concealed circuit leads to a noiseless switch underneath the box, which can be operated by the experimenter without the subject's knowledge. By means of this switch, the experimenter may shunt the current through the coil or cut the coil out entirely, without affecting the illumination of the lamps.

The subject is instructed: "I want to test your ability to perceive warmth. Hold the coil of wire gently between the thumb and forefingers. You will see that the coil is connected with these lamps so that when I light them, a current can flow through the coil and warm it—it is made of German silver wire and offers a slight resistance to the current. You cannot feel any shock, nothing but slight warmth. Watch carefully and at the moment you feel warmth, say 'Now'."

The secret coil-switch is then closed so that no current passes through the coil. The experimenter then says "Now," snaps the lampswitch rather ostentatiously, starts the stop watch, and leans forward expectantly.

Observe that in the first test, the suggestion is derived by the subject from the object conditions of the experiment, rather than from the attitude, tone, instructions, or personality of the experimenter; but that in the second and third tests, statements are made that are intended to control or influence the judgment that the subject is about to make.

Table 1 shows the results of these three tests. For the purpose of scoring, subjects in all three experiments were considered as having accepted the suggestion if five consecutive positive scores were

TABLE 1. *Results of Tests 1, 2, 3*

THE 5 GROUPS	NO. IN EACH GROUP	NO. ACCEPTING SUGGESTIONS Tests		
		1	*2*	*3*
1. Patients	25	21	20	19
2. Physicians, Professors	25	17	16	16
3. Nurses	25	22	21	20
4. Business Executives	25	18	18	17
5. Students	25	20	21	21
% *total group that gave positive results*		78.3%	77.6%	73.6%

obtained. Of the subjects, 78.3% accepted the suggestion of progressive lengths of lines, 77.6% of alternating lengths of lines, and 73.6% of the illusion of warmth. In the total group of experiments, 77% of the subjects accepted suggestions. The records of the students, nurses and patients were almost identical, and while in general the percentage of acceptance of suggestion is lower in the two other groups, the differences are not significant and may possibly be accounted for by age and experience.

It is of particular interest that the subjects who accepted the suggestion on one of the experiments tended to accept the suggestion on all three experiments, while those who refused the suggestion on one experiment refused the suggestion on all three experiments. Of the total group of 125 subjects, 90 accepted the suggestions on all three tests and 23 refused the suggestions on all three tests. Only 12 subjects, or approximately 10%, were inconsistent, accepting suggestions on one test and refusing suggestions on another test.

From the group of 90 subjects who accepted the suggestions on all three tests, ten were chosen at random for participation in induction of a hypnotic state. The experimenter acted as the hypnotist, and all ten subjects were hypnotized in less than ten minutes, nine in less than five minutes. From the 23 subjects who refused suggestions on all three experiments, five were selected at random for participation in hypnosis. The experimenter again acted as the hypnotist, and only one of the five subjects was hypnotized, and then only at the end of the third half-hour period.

There appeared to be evidence here that the tests indicated general suggestibility and that they also predicted the hypnotizability of the subjects. The most important doubt regarding the results grew out of the recognition that a single experimenter had participated in all of the experiments, and that the same experimenter had made all of the efforts to induce a hypnotic state. It might be possible, therefore, that we were not dealing with general suggestibility or the prediction of hypnotizability except as these facts are related to the relationship between the subject and the experimenter-hypnotist.

Therefore, a second experiment was designed to investigate the same facts when the experimenters are varied. In this experiment, 60 subjects were used, equally divided into three groups of students, nurses, and patients. The same three tests were used, but two new experimenters were added. The experiment was so arranged that each subject did one of the three tests with each experimenter. It was also possible so to regulate the experiments that one-third of the subjects saw each experimenter first and also performed each of the tests first. By controlling the order in which the tests were given and in which the subject came in contact with the experimenters, it was possible to rule out the probability that any of these orders prejudiced the test situations. The scoring of the tests was identical with the scoring in the first experiment.

Table 2 shows the results of the second experiment. Each subject took one of the three tests with each experimenter, and the

TABLE 2. *Results of Second Experiment*

NO. OF SUBJECTS	EXPERIMENTER	POSITIVE RESULTS		NEGATIVE RESULTS
60	A	48	*80%*	12
60	B	38	*63.3%*	22
60	C	39	*65%*	21

Table shows the response of the subjects to each experimenter. Of the subjects, 80% accepted the suggestion from Experimenter A, 63.3% from Experimenter B, and 65% from Experimenter C. If the results of the three experimenters are taken together, 69.4% of the subjects accepted suggestions. Of the 60 subjects used in the experiments, 23 accepted the suggestions from all three experimenters and 6 refused the suggestions from all three experimenters. Thus 29, or slightly less than half, gave consistent responses to all experimenters, while 31, or slightly more than half, varied in their responses to the three experimenters. Of the 31 subjects whose responses varied, all possible patterns were present. Some accepted the suggestion of one experimenter while refusing those of the other two; some accepted the suggestions of two experimenters but refused those of the third, with the third experimenter varying. The results are reported for the total group of 60 subjects, since the responses of the patients, nurses and students were almost identical. There also appeared to be no difference in effectiveness of anyone of the three tests. What is particularly significant is that, in the first experiment when the subjects were responding to a single experimenter, approximately 90% of them gave consistent responses of either acceptance or rejection, whereas in the second experiment, less than half of the group gave consistent responses. It may be hypothesized that the subjects were responding primarily to the experimenter rather than to the test situation.

Unfortunately, the unavailability of the subjects caused the experiment to be closed before the plan could be completed to test their hypnotizability. Only a few were available for the last phase of the experiment. From those available, the following results were obtained:

Three of the subjects scored as suggestible to all three experimenters were hypnotized by all three experimenters. Experimenter A was able to induce a hypnotic state in three subjects scored as suggestible to him and not to the other two experimenters. Neither Experimenter B nor C was able to hypnotize these subjects. Experimenter C was able to hypnotize two subjects whose test results were scored as suggestible to him and not to either of the other experimenters. Both of the other experimenters failed to hypnotize these subjects. Experimenter B was able to hypnotize two subjects whose test results were scored as suggestible to him but not to experimenters A or C. Neither of these subjects could be hypnotized by experimenter C, but one of them was hypnotized by experimenter A. The rest of the subjects were not available for the continuation of the experiment. There appears here further indication that the subjects were responding to the experimenter or hypnotist.

In the course of the experiment, a number of interesting features were noticed. In some instances, the subjects who were responding to the suggestions of longer and shorter lines tended to mark them as longer or shorter while saying, "They all look the same to me." Several subjects in this part of the experiment, after about the fourth statement by the experimenter, were noted to be no longer looking at the aperture but responding only to the experimenter's statements.

It would appear that there is reason to examine further the role of the hypnotist and to consider the hypothesis that quite aside from general suggestibility people are suggestible to one person and negativistic to another. This might be examined in full recognition that the nature of the suggestion as well as the "mental set" of the subject is important in inducing the more complex phenomena of hypnosis. The major missing links in the understanding of hypnotizability are probably to be found in the unconscious needs, wishes, prohibitions, and the like, that influence so greatly all of the person's behavior as well as his response to hypnosis.

REFERENCES

1. Pavlov, I. P.: The identity of inhibition with sleep and hypnosis, Sci Monthly *17*:603-908, 1923.

2. Hull, C. L.: Hypnosis and Suggestibility, New York, Appleton, 1933.

3. Darrow, C. W., *et al.*: Inter-area electroencephalographic relationships affected by hypnosis, preliminary report, Electroenceph Clin Neurophysiol *2*:231, 1950.

4. White, R. W., and Shevach, S.: Hypnosis and concept of dissociation, J Abnorm Soc Psychol *37*:309-328, 1942.

5. Welch, L.: A behavioristic explanation of the mechanism of suggestion and hypnosis, J Abnorm Soc Psychol *42*:359-364, 1947.

6. Kubie, L. J., and Margolin, S.: The process of hypnotism and the nature of the hypnotic state, Amer J Psychiat *100*:611-622, 1944.

7. White, R. W.: A preface to a theory of hypnotism, J Abnorm Soc Psychol *36*:477-506, 1941.

8. Sarbin, T. R.: Contributions to role-taking theory, I. Hypnotic behavior, Psychol Rev *57*:255-270, 1950.

9. West, L. J.: Physiological theories of hypnosis, Transactions of the International Congress of Hypnosis, 1961, pp. 128-130.

10. Arnold, M. B.: Brain function in hypnosis, Int J Clin Exp Hypn *7*:109-119 (#3), 1959.

11. Dorcus, R. M., and Shaffer, G. W.: Textbook of Abnormal Psychology, ed. 4, Baltimore, Williams & Wilkins, 1950.

12. Murphy, G., and Murphy, L. B.: Experimental Psychology, New York, Harper, 1931, p. 136.

13. Triplett, N.: The psychology of conjuring deceptions, Amer J Psychol *2*:439-510, 1900.

14. Small, W. S.: The suggestibility of children, Pediatric Seminar *4*:176-220, 1896.

15. Guidi, G.: Recherches experimentales sur la suggestibilite, Arch Psychol *8*:49-54, 1908.

16. Gilbert, J. A.: Researches on the mental and physical development of school children, Stud Yale Psychol Lab *2*:43-45, 59-63, 1894.

17. Brown, W.: Individual and sex differences in suggestibility, Univ Calif Pub in Psychol *2*:291-430, 1916.

18. Hull, C. L.: Hypnosis and Suggestibility, New York, Appleton, 1933, pp. 41-63.

Discussion

GARY O. MORRIS, MD

Private Practice of Psychiatry, Washington

DR. SHAFFER'S CONTROLLED SECOND STUDY, developed logically from his first, forcibly indicated that both waking suggestibility and susceptibility to hypnosis reflect the subject's relationship with the experimenter instead of representing only individually limited or personality-determined factors of suggestibility.

Over the years, I have received a fairly large number of referrals of patients actively seeking hypnotherapy. Among these supplicants, a large subgroup have tried a variety of treatment techniques, often including psychoanalysis, all of which have failed. In my experience, the patients from this subgroup whom I tried to hypnotize were unhypnotizable. Negativistic patients, such as these, are negativistic to any approach that one may try. Nowadays, I routinely recommend that they try psychotherapy once more with one of my colleagues. This they facilely reject, just as they rejected my efforts at hypnosis of an earlier time.

Most hypnotists begin their training of hypnotic subjects by using relatively standardized tests of waking suggestions. We all make intuitive predictions of the hypnotizability of our subjects from the degree of their positive responses. In addition, such tests are often used as screening procedures to help select good hypnotic subjects.

In my initial work with hypnosis, I worked with a few subjects from volunteers who had been eliminated as hypnotic subjects for another study because of their poor responses to group suggestibility tests. Two of these rejects were excellent hypnotic subjects, illustrating how subjects may respond differently to different situations and experimenters.

A number of clinical and experimental studies indicate the relation between suggestibility and hypnotizability.[1,2] The research probably most applicable to Dr. Shaffer's first study is by Eysenck and Furneaux,[3] who showed a definite correlation between various forms of waking suggestion and hypnotizability. In particular, a positive response by subjects to both a postural sway test and a heat illusion test correlated 0.96 with hypnotizability.

Dr. Shaffer made a statement with which I disagree, i.e., that we have no satisfactory theory of the nature of hypnosis. Speaking from the vantage point of psychoanalytic theory, Schilder and Kauders already had a good theory [4] of the transference nature of hypnosis back in 1925, which included ego-concepts quite advanced for that time. Kubie and Margolin [5] published their innovative theory of the hypnotic process and state in the early 1940's, and Gardner and I have confirmed most of their theories from our observations. We posited a more inclusive theory of hypnosis, which we published in 1959.[6] At the same time, Gill and Brenman [1] published their book on hypnotic theory, which contained many concepts analogous and parallel to ours. These theories all emphasize the importance of the relationship of the hypnotist and subject in determining hypnotizability and in influencing the nature of the transference neurosis during hypnosis.

A few psychologists with basically different theoretical frameworks have also emphasized the importance of the rapport between hypnotist and subject in determining hypnotizability. Whereas Dr. Shaffer's work does not support any theoretical system among the psychoanalysts or those theoretical psychologists as against another, it does emphasize the relationship between positive rapport and hypnotizability.

REFERENCES

1. Gill, M. M., and Brenman, M.: Hypnotherapy: A Survey of the Literature, New York, Internat Univ Press, 1947; and Hypnosis and Related States, New York, Internat Univ Press, 1959.

2. Weitzenhoffer, A. M.: *In* Hypnosis, An Objective Study in Suggestibility, New York, Wiley, 1953.

3. Eysenck, H. J., and Furneaux, W. D.: Primary and secondary suggestibility: an experimental and statistical study, J Exp Psychol *35*:485-503, 1945.

4. Schilder, P.: The Nature of Hypnosis, New York, Internat Univ Press, 1956.

5. Kubie, L. S., and Margolin, S.: The process of hypnotism and the nature of the hypnotic state, Amer J Psychiat *100*:611-622, 1944.

6. Morris, G. O., and Gardner, C. W.: Contributions to the theory of the hypnotic process and the established hypnotic state, Psychiatry *22*:377-398 (#4), Nov, 1959.

5

Auditory Residues in Dreams

DOUGLAS NOBLE, MD

Clinical Professor of Psychiatry,
George Washington University
School of Medicine,
Washington

SEYMOUR J. ROSENBERG, MD

Clinical Professor of Psychiatry,
Georgetown University
School of Medicine,
Washington

Others have observed and discussed the role of verbal day residues in dreams, their relation to superego functioning, and their similarity to auditory hallucinations in schizophrenia.

This is a preliminary report on some experiments in which subjects were exposed in the waking state to "incidental registrations" in the form of fragments of simultaneous scrambled conversations on a tape recorder. Other types of incidental registrations were employed, with the aim of determining whether or not fragments of conversations that were not heard in the waking state were incorporated into later dreams. In a few cases only did this occur, and when it did the day residue entered into the visual structure of the dream and did not appear as an actual speech. Speeches very rarely were recorded by our subjects. Most commonly, circumstances of the experiment itself appeared in dreams, with transference phenomena prominent.

ONE OF FREUD'S EARLIEST REFERENCES to the role of speeches in dreams was in the account [1] of his woman patient who dreamed that when she came to the market to find the meat sold out, the butcher told her: "That's not obtainable any longer." Freud stated that the butcher's remark derived from his explanation to the patient that the earliest experiences of childhood were "not obtainable any longer as such but were replaced in analysis by transferences and dreams." The patient was rejecting these transferences onto the analyst, and the speech in her dream appeared in the crisis evoked by the emergence of unacceptable instinctual impulses. Freud also pointed out [1] that hallucinations may appear when the ego is threatened by bodily danger or by the emergence of *Id* impulses, and described how, when he had had a narrow escape in a mountain accident, he had heard spoken the words: "Now it's all up with you," which he saw written in front of him at the same time.

I.

Freud stated that the speech in a dream is derived from a speech heard on the preceding day, and added [2] that the speech may derive from material read or thought on the day of the dream. The speech may undergo displacement, fragmentation, condensation, or secondary revision. Robert Fliess,[3] extending Freud's ideas, characterized the speech in the dream as a temporary re-establishment of the superego in response to an unconscious wish to reinforce the censor and invoke the superego for protection. It revives, in a crisis, the child's need for parental direction.

Isakower [5] stated that since the nucleus of the superego is auditory, "words in a dream may be a contribution of the super-ego to the dream." He commented on the role of the auditory sphere in the development of reality testing, and stated that the auditory sphere keeps us oriented to the world of conduct in a manner comparable to that performed by the adjacent vestibular system, which keeps us oriented in space. He also stated that "at the moment of waking up, the linguistic auditory phenomena present themselves in a briefer and more succinct form. A word or short sentence still reaches a dreamer while he is waking up like a call; and this call has very often a super-ego tinge, sometimes threatening, sometimes criticizing."

Bertram Lewin [10] described the sound of the alarm clock as waking the sleeper who, weaned from his regressed state to harsh reality, tends to forget his dreams. Jones,[4] Kohut,[8] and Stein [13] have dealt with the frightening aspects of early acoustic experiences and of defenses developed against them. Jones traced the pervasive occurence in mythology of the power and fear of the voice of the father. Kohut, discussing fears of noise in early infancy, suggested that the cultivation of musical interest may evolve in an attempt to overcome such traumata, and that when listening to music we may hear the words and tones of parental commands. Stein described a group of patients with a history of severe ear disturbances in childhood who developed a syndrome in which amnesia for painful experience, a hypertrophy of superego development, and recurrent traumatic dreams were manifest. In forgetting their dreams, these patients mastered the trauma with the denying statement, "It is only a dream."

Scott wrote [14] that noise relates adults to experiences of infancy and to the animal kingdom; bodily noises, snoring and borborygmi may produce gratification in sleep, while the existence of the noise is denied by the sleeper. A group of subjects, studied by Kubie and Margolin, [16] in listening to their own amplified breath sounds passed into a trance state in which significant memories were recovered. L. W. Max [17] described the appearance of action currents in the arms and fingers of deaf people during sleep, which he ascribed to dream conversation. External stimuli of touch, heat and pressure applied to his subjects during sleep led to the production of visual dreams.

Malamud [18] read stories to waking subjects, which they were asked to repeat; material that they omitted sometimes appeared later in their dreams. In a study of dreams and perception, Fisher [11] commented that one of his subjects heard the sound of a rifle shot aimed at a figure in his dream, which he related to the click of the tachistoscope in the experimental setting.

Fox and Robbins [19] prepared on a tape recorder a group of Chinese words paired with their English equivalents, which they played to experimental groups in the waking state and, later, during sleep. They concluded that learning could occur during sleep. Two of their subjects had dreams related to the experiment: one dreamed of a street scene in China, the other that the instructor was reading a list of Chinese words. Oswald [20] *et al.* played spoken names to a group of sleeping subjects, noting EEG responses, and observed that K complexes on the EEG, indicative of arousal, occurred with names recognizable to the subject but not with meaningless syllables. Oswald concluded that absence of responses may have been due to the fact that a cortical analysis of the stimulus had established its lack of import for the individual. Berger [21] found that spoken names known to the subjects and presented at random during REM periods were incorporated into the dream events. (Actual voices were rarely heard in these dreams.)

II.

For some time, we have asked students in our dream seminars to participate in a group experiment on the influence of subliminal visual residues using the Poetzl method—a convincing teaching experience. Later, we carried on occasional group experiments in an attempt to study the influence of incidental auditory residues in dream formation, and have begun some observations on the effects on dream formation of external auditory stimuli during the hypnagogic state and during sleep. We report here some preliminary and somewhat random observations derived from these experiments.

The kind of subliminal exposure that the tachistoscope provides is not possible in an auditory experiment, and other methods of providing low-grade incidental auditory stimuli had to be devised. In the first of these, subjects listened to conversations played on a tape recorder in an adjacent room, of which only murmured fragments were audible. In the second, two simultaneous conversations were prepared on the tape, one of a neutral type, the other in the background and in a low tone of voice containing emotionally charged material. The third experiment was prepared by dictating onto the tape a fragment of a story and playing it at twice the ordinary speed, so the replayed tape sounded like a Donald Duck cartoon. A fourth group of observations was made by playing to subjects, during the hypnagogic state or during sleep, comments or messages of a neutral or personal nature, which were repeated at intervals to a background of soothing music.

Most of the subjects were psychoanalytic candidates or psychiatric residents. In those experiments in which subjects were exposed to auditory stimuli in the waking state, usually during seminars, they were given the instructions: "When you dream tonight, write down your dream and any thoughts you have about it, and bring it to the next seminar." They were told the content of the stimulus at the time of reporting their dreams, and this sometimes evoked further associative connections. Reports were limited, for the most part, to the manifest content, with a few preconscious associations. Those subjects to whom stimuli were given during sleep or the hypnagogic state were asked to cooperate with a research in dreams and told that they would be exposed to some message or music on a tape recorder during the night; they were questioned about dreams on the following morning. We present excerpts from illustrative experiments.

EXPERIMENT 1

Four candidates in a psychoanalytic dream seminar were exposed to a low conversation played on a tape recorder in an adjoining room. Dr. T and Dr. N, the two instructors, were talking.

Dr. N: "How do you like these seminars?" Dr. T: "I'm finding them very boring." Dr. N (with heat): "I have certainly tried to make them interesting." Dr. T: "If you ask me, it is not worth the trouble of driving over here on such a nice day." Three of the four candidates reported dreams. The first, in the waking state, heard, "Well, if you ask me, it is hardly worth the trouble driving over here on such a nice day." He reported the following dream.

> *Dream.* A large, open room, like a motion picture theatre; we are going to be shown a movie about the gay "nighties" and how to play pool. (There is a movie in color going on at the side of the movie theatre; I am not watching this movie, but it is about the same subject.) In the center of the room is a pool table, on the other side a bar. The father comes into the room; everyone focuses attention on him. He states that the demonstration will begin. He picks up a billiard cue, which I note to be much thinner in the shaft than the ordinary cue, and I wonder why he is using that. He shows us how to grasp the cue. A woman in the group makes some statement that it should not be grasped too far up the shaft or it would be too short. I regard this as a bit of comic relief; I know she is referring to the penis and wonder why she is concerned about how you grasp it at the base when I am concerned about the other end of it.
>
> At this point, the group gets smaller, and we are in the front hall of the theatre. My neighbor turns the meeting over to his little boy, who is expected to make a speech. He stands there, playing with his cowboy gun, feeling anxious. His father insists that he do the job, and he stammers out that they are going to show us a TV movie. My thought was: "Is that what is going to happen? Why did they call this a party?" We sit down at a round table in the doorway; the mother is there and has taken my seat. . . . I feel she belongs at home. I wake up, realize it is 6:30 AM, and feel irritated at having to write down the dream for Dr. N. Then I laugh at my dream for being an expression of this irritation.
>
> *Associations.* The situation reminds me of the seminar with Dr. N. The gay "nighties" refers to Dr. Noble's age and to his mannerism of pulling at his chest, as though he wore suspenders. The color movie reminded me that I did not dream when Dr. N showed us a color slide in a previous dream experiment. I had the thought that Dr. N had come here to teach us how to masturbate and not to teach dream theory. Dr. N had reported an anxiety dream in which the dreamer had felt a cold hand on his forehead. Thought of the hand on the penis. Being forced by the father relates to my feeling in childhood that my father was

pushing me too fast. The little boy reminds me of Dr. T's youthful appearance. The conversion of theme from sex to eating expresses one way of handling my oedipal conflicts.

This dream illustrates manifestations that were observed often in our experiments. The setting of the dream resembles the rooms in which the seminars were held. The pleasurable expectations of the instructor condensed the wish for gratification of infantile needs as well as the current wish to learn, which are combined in the reference to the experiment, in the dream, in which "the father shows them how to grasp the cue." The theme of disappointment appears in the manifest dream as well as in the fragment heard from the stimulus, "It's hardly worth the trouble driving over here on such a nice day." Anxieties related to childhood situations were evoked by the experiment.

The second subject distorted the stimulus when hearing it in the waking state. She heard, "Worried—have to trust. If you ask me, it's not worth driving over here on Sunday."

Dream. Two doctors were talking in my presence of matters of little interest to me in a nondescript room. I thought, "I'm not one of them, so I will leave and do it on my own." I was next on a desolate plain galloping straight ahead on a brown horse. This was followed by a third scene at the infirmary on a Sunday morning (the morning of the seminar). I am lying on a stretcher covered by a white sheet surrounded by colored orderlies who wait with me until the doctor comes. The doctor, dressed in a gray suit, says, "You're OK—you must have fallen on your fat fanny." It seemed as if I had dreamed three times (there were three seminars). On awakening, I remembered that it was Sunday and I had to go to the Institute for the class. Not pleased with the idea and remembering the last part of the dream, I thought, "Get off your ass and go to the dream class." I had planned to spend the rest of the day at the beach.

In an earlier oral report of this dream the subject had reported that in the manifest dream someone had spoken to her angrily, saying, "Get off your fat fanny," a statement that later in her written report she ascribed to herself.

Association. The dreamer stated that one of the two doctors in the dream had invited her to a party on the night before; she had declined to attend because of the dream seminar and because she did not like the man. She reported similar mixed feelings for the instructor, who, like the doctor in the dream, wore a gray suit.

She had felt angry the day before when the instructor had used her name in illustration of a discussion about pleasing others; he had said that if she were attending the class to please others, it would be healthier to leave. She also stated that her own analyst had visited her in the hospital when she had had an operation for an abscess in the buttocks. "The doctors talking of matters of little interest to me," she said, "may indicate a feeling of rejection." "In the last seminar, I felt I was not participating much. As to the horse, riding is something I'm learning to do well but with some anxiety as I progress."

In this material, the subject distorted her hearing of the original stimulus in relationship to a personal problem, and modified her second account of the manifest dream, where she ascribed to herself the harsh comment made by the doctor in the initial dream report. The feeling of rejection, related in the dream to the doctors' conversation that was of no interest to her, was dealt with first by her galloping off and "Doing it on her own," later by a wish-fulfilling scene at the infirmary on a Sunday morning, the morning of the seminar in which the doctor visits her personally. The appearance of the speech in the dream appears to relate to the emergence of ambivalent emotions in the transference to the instructor, tending to confirm Fliess's idea that speeches occur when some powerful instinctual feeling is arising. There is a resemblance to the experimental setting in the room in the dream. The dreamer's feeling that she has dreamed three times related to the three scenes of her dream and to the fact that, at that time, there had been three seminars. In the reference to riding, she was turning to an activity in which she was more active and more successful than in the dream studies.

The third subject heard a garbled conversation between two men and then heard Dr. T state, "If you ask me, it's too much trouble driving over here."

Dream: I had purchased a boat, which I was testing with another man. I was in the bow of the boat pouring gas through a small opening. . . . I felt the boat was running well but burned a great deal of gas.

Associations: I thought of the expression of "gassing" used by my mother and grandmother. I would rather have been on my boat instead of gassing around the Institute on such a nice day. I recalled that my mother did little "gassing" in response to my approaches during her depression following my father's death.

Feelings that I have had little to offer in discussion of the material relate to childhood problems.

EXPERIMENT 2

In the second group of experiments, two simultaneous conversations were prepared on the tape recorder. Generally, the voice in the foreground spoke of neutral topics, while in the background a conversation dealing with conflictual material was carried on in a lower key. The instructions for the experiment were similar to those of Experiment 1. Group and individual experiments were carried out with the following findings. *1.* Out of 69 subjects tested in the series, 31 reported dreams. (These figures, however, must be judged in the light of the fact that the interest of participants in the course and in the instructor greatly influenced the frequency of dreams.) *2.* In the dreams reported (again studied in their manifest content and preconscious associations), references to the experiment or to the experimenter occurred in about 50% of instances. *3.* Occasionally the affect of the conversation was caught by the subject, as in one experiment given to a subject individually, where in the foreground two girls were talking pleasantly about their summer vacation while in the background two men were criticizing Dr. N's dream course. One said, "It is a very boring course." The other replied, "It's not worthwhile coming down here when the driving is so dangerous. It's like taking your life in your hands." The subject heard, in the waking state, "Two girls talking optimistically and two men talking pessimistically." He reported a dream in which he was "outside a house . . . heard noises, people talking." In association, he recalled overhearing similar conversations between the parents in childhood, usually dealing with financial matters; the mother was always optimistic and the father pessimistic.

In other instances, the affect of the stimulus was reversed in the dream material. *4.* Occasionally, the connection between dream and stimulus was not recognized until the dream was reported and the stimulus heard. *5.* In one case, the experiment was followed by the appearance of not a dream but a symptom. A stimulus had been played with a pleasant conversation in the foreground and a reference in the background to an accident on snowy mountain roads. This reference the subject did not hear. On the way home from the seminar, however, he found himself driving with extraordinary care, frequently looking for snow on the roads, which were actually clear. *6.* Speeches were rarely heard in the dream material (in less than 10% of the dreams reported) and when they did occur usually related to the emergence of anxiety-provoking experience. One subject, exposed to the stimulus in which the two girls talked pleasantly while in the background two men criticized the dream course, had the following dream: "My wife and I were in the cafeteria. . . . a man said to my wife, 'Do you have intercourse with your husband?' She replied indignantly, 'Of course, I do,' The man left . . . I was disturbed by the event . . . did not know what it meant. The cafeteria was like a college or hospital. . . . I thought my wife may have met this man before our marriage." This subject, like all of those to whom the stimulus was given in a military hospital, heard no reference to the criticism of the instructor, but when the stimulus that had preceded his dream was played back to him, he related the phrase, "This is a boring course," to the speech, "Do you have *intercourse* with your husband?" in the dream. *7.* Auditory stimuli were almost always transformed into visual dreams. Sometimes this was very impressive, as with one subject who dreamed that he was turning a corner and came to a heap of furnishings. He drew a picture of this heap, although not requested to do so, and related the incline to the rising voice, the crescendo, in the stimulus. *8.* In about a quarter of the dreams reported in this group, references to elements of the stimulus not heard in the waking state appeared in the dream. By way of illustration, a subject was given a stimulus in which in the foreground Dr. R was repeating instructions for the carrying out of an experiment, while in the background the voices of Dr. N and his daughter were heard. The daughter was saying, "Why do I have to be in at 12:30?" Dr. N: "You know we decided on that." Daughter: "Why can't I be in at one o'clock?" Dr. N: "Jay's brother had an accident in the mountains; we don't want it to happen again; we don't want anybody to be dead." In the waking state, the subject heard the voice of Dr. R giving instructions and in the background a discussion between a man, Dr. N, and a woman. "It was not clear what the woman said; she sounded angry." The subject dreamed.

> *Dream.* I and my wife and friends were at a street intersection standing on a high bank. Numerous automobile accidents were occurring. It was gory. There were viscera, all that remained of the people. My wife slipped off the bank while watching. I caught her and eased her down and jumped after her, a 10 or 12 foot drop.

Associations. The tape seemed silly, the dream serious, I doubt if there was any connection. My daughter would not go to sleep that night; perhaps the accident meant her death. We were running off the deep bank, away from responsibility.

EXPERIMENT 3

In this experiment, a story was prepared on the tape recorder that dealt with a man who was wandering in the woods, then leaned against a tree when he was stabbed in the back and robbed. This story was played to subjects at double the ordinary speed, so that it sounded like a Donald Duck cartoon. A wide difference occurred in what was heard of the stimulus by the subjects in the waking state. Several of them heard practically nothing; one subject heard almost the entire content of the stimulus. Twelve out of 20 subjects reported dreams. In four cases, there were references in the manifest dream material to contents of the stimulus that were not heard in the waking state. Three subjects reported speeches in their dreams. One of them was much impressed by what he said was the first auditory experience he had ever recalled having in a dream. He had not recalled hearing clearly any message in the stimulus. "My dream was one of eavesdropping. I was lying in bed in the third story of my house and heard a woman's voice say, 'The house looks better now, at least, than it did.' I felt that two middle-aged women were walking below but did not have a visual impression of them." In association, the patient said that a new window had recently been placed in his house but that he had had it changed against the advice of the architect. In other words, the dreamer was receiving reassurance from a mother figure that he had dealt successfully with a situation of conflict with the male authority.

Another subject stated that the recording was absolutely unintelligible, but "there was an impression of a statement about a man. I thought I heard the word 'repeatedly.' Once I thought I heard 'bank,' an impression of a robber."

Dream. I was walking in the woods with my wife, perhaps lost. I came into an open place where a man stripped to the waist was standing. He was a painter and had painted a self-portrait in the nude. His hand was on his penis. He seemed to be a suspicious character, and I feared he might attack us and sexually assault my wife. She seemed unaware of the danger. I remember having a gun and being prepared to use it. I had murderous impulses.

The man was white and well built. In the painted picture he was lying on his back at a 45° angle, leaning against a tree.

The last statement was taken directly from the original stimulus and had not been heard by the subject. The dream made a strong impression on the subject, so that he made a drawing of the position in which the man was lying, the unheard part of the stimulus, and brought it with him to the seminar. (A third subject, a medical student, reported hearing the stimulus as follows: "Daddy . . . gasp . . . please . . . unintelligible. It was fast dictated speech.")

Dream. Medical students were waiting for something. Suddenly a person, I think myself, stands at the counter in the bank. A voice tells me, "The bank is protected. You are secure here."

EXPERIMENT 4

A. In this experiment a superego type of stimulus with words of warning was placed on the tape on a background of soft music. Five subjects were tested, and two reported dreams. The first subject, a nurse, heard the stimulus, "Driving is dangerous; take care," while the experimenters were preparing it. Although she heard the stimulus accidentally she was asked to report a dream.

Dream. The subject dreamed that she was expected to report a dream.

The second subject was given the stimulus just before falling asleep. She reported the next day having heard nothing but the background music.

Dream: I was driving by myself. I was a very small person . . . lots of people around . . . some gave advice. . . . had trouble tripping over the end of my skis on a mountain as I walked. . . . I got onto a rope tow and went up high on the mountain. There were gigantic vehicles and a building. Part of the building is a lunch counter. I ordered waffles with strawberries. There was a change. I was no longer the character in the dream. There was a boy, my little brother. He and the restaurant man talked about the need for exercise. (*Note.* The manifest dream content includes references to driving, which was in the warning stimulus and to the giving of advice.)

B. Similar experiments were carried out with small groups of subjects during sleep. In the first of these the stimulus of soft music in the background with occasional statements, "Don't do that . . . don't touch," were given to three residents and to one mildly depressed patient on the psychiatric service. The patient, to whom the stimulus was given three times, slept throughout the experiment and did not report a dream. One of the residents awakened sufficiently during sleep to hear some words on the tape, which he did not identify. He did not report a dream. Another resident awoke to hear a portion of the music, which he identified and then went back to sleep. He did not hear any words in the stimulus. He wrote down the following dream in the morning.

> *Dream.* I walked into the front office adjacent to the library. The librarian said, "We are going to check up on books which are overdue." I was upset and left the room.
>
> *Associations.* Several months ago my boss inspected a book I was taking from the library to see if I had signed for it properly. I resented this. I have ordered several books from the bookstore and have postponed paying the bill. My wife has been nagging me about it.

Another resident reported hearing music but nothing else.

> *Dream.* "I was hanging four pictures in color, bright colors, red and others." In association, the subject stated that his wife had complained to him on the preceding evening about three pictures standing on the floor, which had been waiting some time to be hung. The subject did not associate to the figures three or four.

Although two of these subjects reported dreams concerned with tasks unperformed, these dreams might just as easily have been stimulated by residues from the previous day as by the experimental stimulus. No conclusions can be drawn from these experiments except that these superego stimuli doubtless activate conflictual experiences similar to what Morris has described in his experiments with hypnotized subjects.[22]

c. Another subject convalescing from a depression was believed to be concerned about his wife's pregnancy. On a background of soft music played for several minutes, he was given the suggestion, "Dream about your wife's pregnancy." The subject awoke, heard the music and the message and did not report a dream. His roommate, who slept through the stimulus, reported, however, a dream on the following morning.

> *Dream.* There was a mouse in a cave growing to the size of a rat. There were other rats growing. One was scratching the body of a woman. This reminded me of a nightmare I had several years ago when I woke up in the night thinking I had choked my

wife. No further associations were elicited to this symbolic dream.

D. In another experiment, while asleep against a background of soft music seven inpatients were given the message, "Dream about your problem," repeated several times. The first subject was a 29-year-old man with a hand-washing compulsion and mild symptoms of transvestism. He reported hearing nothing while asleep, but immediately after the tape recorder had been turned off awoke with a feeling of suffocation and a strong feeling "that all he could smell was rose perfume." He left his room immediately and sought reassurance from the nurse's aide, saying that he thought it possible that the experimenters had sprayed perfume into his room as part of the experiment. When questioned the next morning about this nocturnal experience, which appeared to be an olfactory dream, the subject provided no additional information. He did not recall knowing anyone who used perfume of that kind.

The next subject, a 35-year-old man with anxiety and some alcoholism, slept through the stimulus. The next morning, he reported a dream of being in Hawaii fixing a carburetor. He also stated that he had fallen out of bed though the nurses on duty did not confirm this. He produced no associations to the dream except that he had never been in Hawaii.

The four other subjects did not report dreams. This was also true of an additional inpatient, a middle-aged man in a state of mild depression, to whom the same stimulus was given on three separate occasions. He slept through the experiments and did not report any dreams.

III.

In reviewing the observations reported here, we were impressed by the high percentage of subjects who reported dreams. This must be related, however, to the fact that many of them were psycho-analytic candidates, accustomed to studying their dreams. In those experiments in which stimuli were given during the waking state, about half the dreams reported contained references to the experimenters or to the experimental setting. These allusions appeared in visual form, perhaps, as Fisher's experiments suggested, because of the transference onto the experimenter of an unconscious wish that became combined with visual residues from the experiment, subliminally perceived. Auditory residues from the stimuli were incorporated into dreams, but less commonly than were residues from the experimental setting. Auditory residues related both to elements of the stimuli that were consciously perceived in the waking state and to some not perceived. These residues had sometimes undergone distortion or fragmentation before incorporation into the dream, where they usually appeared not as auditory experiences but as visual images. Speeches were reported in something less than 10% of dreams, and when they did occur there was usually evidence that anxiety had been aroused by the emergence of unacceptable impulses. (As Fliess had stated, the speech served a combination of superego and ego functions). The experience described by Freud with the patient whose dream contained a speech derived from something said to her by the analyst is probably not too often observed.

In those experiments in which stories were played on the tape at twice the ordinary speed, there was a striking difference in what was heard by subjects in the waking state. Some of them found the Donald Duck type of recording completely unintelligible; others heard almost the whole story. This doubtless reflects the ability of people to detect concealed evidences of communication in emphases and tone of voice, and we wonder whether there was also some similarity here to a quality often seen in children who play and talk freely with other children who speak a different language. Suzanne Langer has stated that with young children phonemes persist from early infancy, which are suited to the learning of any language and may make it possible for a child to learn several languages at once. Can it be that some adults have retained remnants of these precursors of speech?

The findings that unperceived auditory residues enter into dream formation must be accepted with reservations, since people do not always remember what they have heard; they may not also remember their dreams. On the other hand, since the studies were primarily concerned with manifest content and preconscious associations, it is more than likely that a more thorough study of the dreams reported would have revealed more allusions to the incidental auditory perceptions. In future experiments we plan to submit a number of dreams to detailed investigation and to arrange for an independent observer to match the stimuli with the dreams reported.

There were occasional instances when messages to which subjects had been exposed during sleep were incorporated into their dreams, but these observations clearly require investigation in the sleep laboratory. We hope to pursue experiments of this kind with particular reference to the content of the non-REM periods in which verbal and abstract material is often found.

The question of the transformation of auditory perception to the visual experience of the dream is of interest. We are constantly listening to sound during the day and night, and it is well-known that external auditory stimuli may awaken a sleeper or be incorporated into a dream. This suggests that there is a constant process of selection going on during sleep, as well as of sounds in the daytime. In his recent study, Kubie has described this selection from what he calls the Preconscious Stream. The work of Oswald, who demonstrated that sounds are subjected to cortical analysis, would confirm the idea of such a selection. Perhaps we require a certain feedback from sounds during sleep, since we may awaken when sounds to which we are accustomed cease. Kohut [8,9] has suggested that subjects classify sounds into those that are frightening and those that are soothing, and that we employ during sleep a hysterical denial of external sound. (Morris, in one of his experiments, described a subject who, during a stage of hypnotism, focused his eyes on a shadow on the hypnotist's sleeve. In so doing, he was able to deny the voice of the hypnotist, which irritated him while at the same time he incorporated the hypnotist's commands.) In general, it would seem that sounds of enteroceptive origin have a somnolescent influence providing a form of gratification that preserves sleep and that certain, though not all, external sounds have an arousing or frightening influence. One of my patients recently incorporated the sound of the alarm clock into a dream image of a stern figure who was interfering with his love-making. In our own experiments, the meaningful character of the transformation from the vocal to the visual experience was evidenced by two subjects, who, without being asked to do so, made drawings of elements in their dreams that were related to auditory stimuli.

From the experiments we have made so far, we believe that auditory residues, both perceived and unperceived, are incorporated into dream formation, usually in visual form, and that in the experimental dreams transference elements play a most important role. Our experiments have stimulated several ideas for further investigation, which we hope to pursue in more intensive dream analysis and laboratory studies.

REFERENCES

1. Freud, S.: The Interpretation of Dreams, Standard Edition, New York, Basic, 1963, p. 21.
2. ———: A Metapsychological Supplement to the Theory of Dreams, Standard Edition, vol. 14, pp. 222-235.
3. Fliess, R.: On the spoken word in the dream, *in* The Revival of Interest in the Dream, chap. 10, New York, Internat Univ Press, 1953.
4. Jones, E.: Madonna's conception through the ear, *in* Essays in Applied Psychoanalysis, vol. 2, London, Hogarth, 1951, pp. 266-357.
5. Isakower, O.: On the exceptional position of the auditory sphere, Int J Psychoanal *20*:340-348, 1939.
6. ———: Spoken words in dreams, Psychoanal Quart *23*:1-6, 1954.
7. Waelder, R.: Report of panel B dream theory and interpretation, Bull Amer Psychoanal Ass *5*:(#2)36-40, 1949.
8. Kohut, H.: Observations on the psychological functions of music, J Amer Psychoanal Ass *5*:380-407, 1957.
9. Kohut, H., and Levarie, S.: On the enjoyment of listening to music, Psychoanal Quart *19*:64-87, 1950.
10. Lewin, B.: Phobic systems and dream interpretation, Psychoanal Quart *21*:295-322, 1952.
11. Fisher, C.: Dreams and perception, J Amer Psychoanal Ass *2*:389-445, 1954.
12. ———: A study of the preliminary stages of the construction of dreams and images, J Amer Psychoanal Ass *5*:5-60, 1957.
13. Stein, M.: States of consciousness in the analytic situation, *in* Drives, Affects and Behavior, vol. 2, New York, Internat Univ Press, pp. 60-86.
14. Scott, W. C. M.: Noise, speech and technique, Int J Psychoanal *39*:108-111, 1958.
15. Kubie, L.: A reconsideration of thinking, the dream process, and the dream, Psychoanal Quart *35*:191-198, 1966.
16. Kubie, L., and Margolin, S.: A physiological method of induction of states of partial sleep, Trans Amer Neurol Ass *68*:136-139, 1942.
17. Max, L. W.: Action current responses in deaf mutes, J Comp Physiol Psychol *19*:469-486, 1935.
18. Malamud, W.: Dream analysis: its application in research, Arch Neurol Psychiat *31*:356-372, 1934.
19. Fox, B. H., and Robbins, J. S.: The retention of material presented during sleep, J Exp Psychol *43*:75-79, 1952.
20. Oswald, E. T., et al.: Discriminative responses to stimulation during human sleep, Brain *83*:440-453, 1960.
21. Berger, R. J.: Experimental modification of dream content to meaningful, verbal stimuli, Brit J Psychiat *109*:722-740, 1963.
22. Morris, G., and Gardner, C. W.: Contributions to the theory of the hypnotic process, Psychiatry *22*:377-398, 1959.

Discussion

Frederick Snyder, MD

*Chief, Section on Psychophysiology of Sleep, Adult Psychiatry Branch,
National Institute of Mental Health,[1] Bethesda*

Provoking many thoughts, Dr. Noble's chapter has excited in me the possibility of an entirely new approach to projective testing, based on ambiguous auditory stimuli rather than visual stimuli. This occurred to me just yesterday, in the NIH cafeteria, noisier even than usual because of renovations. As I was meditating there, an attractive young lady came by my table and shouted to a young man several tables away. I heard her say: "You're working your tail off." The young man smiled agreement and shouted back: "Yeah, I know, but I'm going to get some more over the weekend." Well, I pondered that little dialogue awhile, with appropriate reflections about the younger generation, until it finally occurred to me that what she must have actually said was: "You're working your tan off."

Two years after the founding of Sheppard Pratt, there was another beginning in this country, the true beginning, I think, of the scientific study of dreaming. Of course, there had been innumerable learned writings about this subject before, but for the most part they followed a different pattern, elaborate edifices of speculation built on flimsy foundations of anecdote, the more extraordinary the better. In contrast to this method, still largely dominating our clinical writing, and which I think of as the *mirabile dictu* approach, the investigation I refer to was unspectacular, uncontroversial, and by now is almost forgotten. The author was an instructor at Wellesley College named Mary Whiton Calkins, and the approach she used was the essence of simplicity and the scientific method. She merely took the pains to write down

[1] US Department of Health, Education and Welfare, Public Health Service, National Institutes of Health.

118

every remembered feature of her own dreams after spontaneous awakenings, and persuaded a male colleague to do the same. The only instruments employed were paper, pencils, candles and matches. In just a few weeks, they collected 375 dreams in this manner, which Miss Calkins then proceeded to classify and examine in a systematic, organized and comprehensive manner, which could still serve as a model of scientific exposition for present-day dream researchers.

I think that we are just beginning to obtain sufficient information from our present techniques to appreciate the remarkable validity of her conclusions, but I'll mention the most general of them. When all remembered dreams, and not merely the beguiling or peculiar ones, were exhaustively recorded immediately after they had occurred, the striking thing was their very prosaic and ordinary nature, directly and simply reflecting mundane preoccupations of daily life. None of us lately have undertaken the kind of systematic analysis that she first employed, but my impression from examining many hundreds of dream reports obtained in the laboratory over the past seven years is precisely the same.

The point of this vignette would be commonplace with regard to almost any other subject matter, but has been peculiarly overlooked with respect to the study of dreaming as a natural phenomenon, i.e., that the essence of the scientific approach has little to do with the complexity of instruments, techniques, or hypotheses, but is entirely a matter of systematic, unselective, and dedicated observation. I belabor this point because I feel that it is so well exemplified in the work that Dr. Noble has described. In these respects, that work is in the best tradition of the Sheppard Pratt hospital and of the almost equally venerable tradition of American dream research.

In all likelihood, my two best credentials for discussing this excellent chapter were not among the reasons why I was invited to do so. The first of these is that practically all of my formal education relating to the psychodynamics of dreams was taught by Doctors Noble and Rosenberg in their course at the Washington Psychoanalytic Institute some years ago, and the second is that I was a subject in certain of the experiments described. I was one of those, alas, who did not remember dreaming. By comparison, the part that I have played in the newly developing investigation of laboratory sleep and dreaming is hardly a recommendation, for although the research techniques involving physiological monitoring and the immediate collection of dream reports would be ideally suited, thus far they have not been applied to the issues that these studies have dealt with. Perhaps some of the things we have learned about the nature of dreaming in the past decade or so may be of peripheral relevance, and the rest of my comments will be from that general perspective.

I am among those who claim that the research of the past 14 years or so has provided a new conception of dreaming as the subjective aspect of a distinct biological state, and we are in the midst of a headlong rush of investigation to encompass this third state. Time and much further study will decide whether that is a useful point of view, but in the meantime we are also provided with a method by which the direct study of dreaming consciousness can be more closely approximated than ever before. Yet many very basic questions concerning the subjective aspects of this phenomenon have not yet been subjected to this method. I can only express my regret that laboratory dream researchers have not contributed to these worthy efforts, and my admiration for the manner in which the scientific dedication and ingenuity of Drs. Noble and Rosenberg have circumvented this limitation.

The concern of this paper with auditory elements in dreaming prompted me to reflect on the general phenomenology of dreaming as an experiential state. When dream recall is obtained by experimental awakenings from REM periods, it generally displays a vividness and wealth of detail such as is seldom found in spontaneously remembered dreams, but the opportunity that this presents for the intensive study of the phenomenology of dreaming consciousness has been scarcely exploited. One aspect systematically studied is the matter of color in the dreaming. Earlier studies of the incidence of color in spontaneously recalled dreams produced estimates ranging from 14% to 29%, and when dreams involving color were reported in therapy it was reason for psychodynamic speculation. I commented in 1960 that almost regularly when experimental subjects remembered their dreams vividly, they recalled at least some elements in color. Kahn and his co-workers soon documented this by showing that color could be demonstrated in 83% of REM reports if subjects were discretely questioned about the details of their dream experiences, although this incidence dropped markedly even within a minute after the end of the REM periods. Several subsequent studies have reported entirely similar results. Apparently it is the special fragility of dream memory that casts the gray pall over dreaming.

This is simply an example of the kind of approach that would be applicable to many aspects of dreaming consciousness, and even though no comparable study has been done with regard to auditory elements in dreaming, the same kind of inference probably applies. Unless I misread them, psychoanalytic discussions of auditory elements in reported dreams seem to imply that these are unusual and particularly significant manifestations. Perhaps they are in spontaneous dream recall; but they are not in laboratory dream reports. Dr. Noble's chapter prompted me to do a very cursory examination of a small sample of the reports collected in our laboratory over the past years, although they had not been obtained with this purpose in mind. The content of most of these dream reports involved two or more people in interaction, and almost invariably that interaction included a description of conversation. Occasionally details about tone of voice are mentioned, and with appropriate questioning this could be studied more carefully, but for the present we can only infer that these conversations were auditory experiences. Of a total of 166 reports from ten subjects, verbal interaction was described in 63%. Something about the nature of the conversation was detailed in most instances, and in 16% ostensibly verbatim elements were reported. Music, singing or laughing were also described, but much less frequently.[1] If we were to do a study of the incidence of conspicuous auditory elements in time samples of waking experience, this might well be in the same range. This is not a new thesis, for such authors as Calkins, Weed and Hallem or Bentley, who systematically recorded dream experience immediately after nocturnal awakenings, reported entirely comparable results 50 to 70 years ago. Memory for the auditory aspects of dreams, like that for color,

[1] Inspired by this same interest, we have since done a much more systematic examination of 635 REM dream reports from 58 subjects and 250 subject nights. Verbal interaction was spontaneously mentioned in 76% of these (100% in a subgroup classified as "long" reports). Something was said about the content of speech in 59% of the total, and alleged quotations were offered in 26%. These descriptions of verbal interaction do not necessarily prove the existence of auditory imagery during dreaming, though many instances were hardly amenable to any other explanation—for example, a report involving eavesdropping on a discussion in the next room, or another in which a noisy conversation in the background suddenly stopped.

seems to be quite evanescent, and therefore those fragments that do survive may be particularly significant. My point is that the dearth of instances in which Noble and Rosenberg were able to identify auditory residues in the reports of their experimental subjects is not negative evidence regarding their occurrence in dreaming.

I do not assume, however, that auditory residues of incidentally perceived stimuli would be more likely found in laboratory dream reports. Without any personal experience in studying either the auditory or the visual versions of the so-called Poetzl phenomenon, I have much the same reaction to these studies as I have to reports concerning extrasensory perception. With all due respect to their authors, I cannot help surmising that there must be alternative explanations for such phenomena. An application of the REM monitoring techniques and "in situ" dream collection might be expected to yield more definitive evidence concerning that subject than any previously reported, but if any such application has been made, certainly none has been published. In the five-year interval between 1956 and 1961, at least ten papers were published relating to the Poetzl phenomenon, the last of these being the methodological criticism and experimental refutation by Johnson and Eriksen. As far as I am aware, there has been no reply to that paper, and just two studies concerned with that phenomenon have appeared in the past five years, both failing to demonstrate it. The fact that it has not been studied using dream-monitoring techniques may be simply because so many new issues have come to the fore in the meantime, but it may also reflect the fact that new knowledge of dreaming places a further burden on the credulity of the Poetzl experiment. Even assuming that stimuli not perceived in awareness are somehow registered in our brains and somehow provide substance for the scripts of our dreams, it would seem that this event takes place countless times in everyday experience, and that such registration must be manifest at innumerable points in the 90 minutes or so of nightly dreaming. It must be explained, then, how it occurs that one particular moment of such experience happens to be manifest in the particular fragment of dreaming that happens to be remembered the next day and reported to the experimenter.

A plausible answer might be that these are not matters of chance. Perhaps the experimental stimulus had a very special significance owing to the character of the subjects' involvement with the experimenter, somehow determining that this stimulus either overshadowed all others throughout the subsequent period of dreaming, or that this influence determined which discrete fragment of dreaming was registered in waking memory. The counterpart of the first explanation would be the findings of Stovya concerning the effects of presleep hypnotic suggestion on the REM dream reports of good hypnotic subjects. Of 162 dreams reported by 16 subjects, 70% contained elements showing a clear connection with the suggestion.

Concerning the second possibility, there can be no doubt that the dreams that we ordinarily remember in our waking lives are a highly selected sample of our total dreaming experience, and in any situation in which we attempt to make inferences from spontaneously remembered dreams, whether clinical or experimental, we should wonder why that particular fragment happened to be remembered. No doubt, all of the usually conceptualized psychodynamic factors affect these matters, but there are probably others of a much simpler nature. While the survival of dream memories into the next day is determined by time and nature of awakening, which may be fortuitous, it may also be determined by the inner events themselves. Some years ago I had a subject who had been trained in autohypnosis by her physician father, and I asked her to suggest various kinds of dreams to herself, which I would then collect from REM awakenings. I especially remember her "funny dream" category, for on that particular night every REM awakening yielded elaborately contrived "funny" dreams, almost like a child's first attempt at humor. But even more interesting, I didn't have to awaken her at all. She spontaneously awakened, after 10 or 15 minutes of each REM period, in order to tell me about her dreams.

I suspect that one overriding factor determining our more lasting registration of certain dream experiences, once we have awakened, is simply the degree to which they capture our interest or curiosity. Have you ever heard any one say: "Let me tell you about the uninteresting dream I had last night"? If such factors were not at work, the old observation that patients dream in accordance with their therapists' varied expectations would be much less credible in the light of present knowledge, and obviously the same might apply to experimental subjects who just happen to remember that small portion of their total dream experiences that fits the hypothesis of the experimenter. Dr. Noble has alluded to the transference factors at work in his studies, but I would venture to suggest that they may be the phenomena of primary interest in such studies, as well as in clinical dream reports generally.

It has long been known with regard to hypnotic subject, and Martin Orne has argued that it is true of most experimental subjects, that they go to fantastic lengths to oblige the experimenter, regardless of how he relates to them or how he attempts to disguise his expectations. In the interest of shoring up the scientific foundation of the Poetzl phenomenon, Shevrin and Luborsky demonstrated that the same manifestations could be obtained even from the subjects who did not remember a dream if one simply instructed them to have a daydream. Regardless of the validity of the claim by Johnson and Eriksen that the same elements could be found with equal frequency in subjects who had never been exposed to the subliminal target stimulus, if this phenomenon can be demonstrated in consciously contrived fantasies then there is no assurance that it has anything to do with nocturnal dreaming at all.

Perhaps the *mirabile dictu* phase of dream investigation has come to a close. Dreaming is no longer the mysterious will-o'-the-wisp that has so long titillated the imaginations of otherwise sober scientists. Now it is just another natural event, almost directly accessible and amenable to tediously systematic, controlled and reproducible investigation. Although many venerable issues are still untouched by this approach, we can resign ourselves to the idea that they will be relentlessly engulfed before very long. Within a single decade, the detached embrace of science has extended both outwardly to the moon and inwardly to dreaming. On both counts our poetry starved souls are that much poorer.

REFERENCES

1. Bentley, M.: The study of dreams. A method adapted to the seminary, Amer J Psychol 26:196-210, 1915.

2. Calkins, M. W.: Statistics of dreams, Amer J Psychol 5:311-343, 1893.

3. Johnson, H., and Eriksen, C. W.: Preconscious perception: A re-examination of the Poetzl phenomenon, J Abnorm Soc Psychol 62:497-503, 1961.

4. Kahn, E., Dement, W., and Fisher, C.: Incidence of color in immediately recalled dreams, Science 137:1054-1055, 1962.

5. Orne, M. T.: The nature of hypnosis: Artifact and essence, J Abnorm Soc Psychol 58:277-299, 1959.

6. Pulver, S. E., and Eppes, B.: The Poetzl phenomenon: Some further evidence, J Nerv Ment Dis 136:527-534, 1963.

7. Shevrin, H., and Luborsky, L.: The measurement of preconscious perception in dreams and images: An investigation of the Poetzl phenomenon, J Abnorm Soc Psychol 56:285-294, 1958.

8. Snyder, F.: Dream recall, respiratory variability and depth of sleep, paper delivered at Roundtable on Dream Research, Annual Mtg Amer Psychiat Assn, May, 1960.

9. ———: The new biology of dreaming, Arch Gen Psychiat (Chicago) 8:381-391, 1963.

10. ———: The organismic state associated with dreaming, *in* Greenfield, Norman S., and Lewis, William C., eds.: Psychoanalysis and Current Biological Thought, Madison, Univ Wisconsin Press, 1965, pp. 275-315.

11. Stovya, J. M.: Posthypnotically suggested dreams and the sleep cycle, Arch Gen Psychiat (Chicago) 12:287-294, 1965.

12. Waxenberg, S. E., Dickes, R., and Gottesfeld, H.: The Poetzl phenomenon re-examined experimentally, J Nerv Ment Dis 135:387-398, 1962.

13. Weed, S. C., and Hallam, F. M.: Minor studies from the psychological laboratory of Wellesley college. III. A study of the dream consciousness, Amer J Psychol 7:405-411, 1896.

DR. NOBLE:

I am most appreciative of Dr. Snyder's thoughtful discussion, but cannot reply adequately to it without the careful reading that it deserves. I shall therefore limit myself to one or two comments. First, the possibility cannot be denied of alternative explanations for the appearance in dreams of registrations from the experimental stimuli. Suggestion and transference are certainly involved, and a more accurate estimate of the role of the auditory stimuli must await further experiments in the sleep laboratory.

Second, I was interested in Dr. Snyder's statement that both color and speech in dreams are much more common than is usually believed, that you find both if you look for them. This may well be true. It may also be, since both color and speech in dreams seem to be associated with the emergence of strong emotion, that they are both subject to inhibition in the manner characteristic of the suppression of affects. Thus, by the dream work, both color and speech may not be readily apparent but may be manifested on enquiry or when the dream work begins to fail in its functioning.

Innovators?

KENT E. ROBINSON, MD
Director of the Outpatient Services,
The Sheppard and Enoch Pratt Hospital, Towson

I HAVE BEEN IMPRESSED here by two themes, one the nostalgic reminiscence about the old days at Sheppard Pratt, the other the general proposition that there isn't much new under the sun. As to nostalgia, I am somewhat envious, because, having been here full time only the last two years, I can't reminisce. As to new things under the sun, I did feel, when I came to Sheppard Pratt, that I was starting many new things—new at least to Sheppard Pratt.

As Director of Outpatient Services, I felt that we were innovators in broadening our residency training program to include adult and children's outpatient clinics and in supplying the student mental health services to Towson State and Morgan State colleges. We are also, in effect, supplying the Psychiatric Department for the neighboring general hospital, the Greater Baltimore Medical Center, a 400-bed teaching hospital. Under the direction of Dr. Schulz and Dr. Drinkard, our residents are also gaining experience with another kind of patient population through their work at the Maryland Training School for Boys.

Because these programs have started within the past two years, you can understand that I might have felt that a number of things were new under Sheppard Pratt's sun. But a few months ago, I was doing a clinic intake interview on a 53-year-old man. He told me that ever since his Bar Mitzvah 40 years ago, he had had a crippling phobia of being afraid that he would faint if he had to talk to groups of more than two or three people, and because he was a furniture salesman, this phobia had made his life difficult. He was all right if just a husband and wife came in to buy furniture, for example, but if mother and father came along to make a group of four, he became very anxious. So I started to explain to him that the outlook for psychotherapy's helping in a case of such long

126

standing was not hopeful. He let me know that he didn't want to hear any of that nonsense about psychotherapy. He knew perfectly well what he needed and it wasn't psychotherapy. He needed two sessions of hypnotherapy, and he had had two sessions 30 years before. No, it hadn't cured his phobia, but it had done him enough good to enable him to carry on as a salesman ever since. The reason he had come back to see a doctor, he said, was that he had had to change jobs to a new store, and he thought that he had better have two more sessions of hypnotherapy so that he could get by on the new job.

"Who referred you to us for hypnotherapy?" I asked, "because just now we are not set up for hypnotherapy." He answered, "Nobody referred me." So I asked, "Well, how did you happen to hear about the clinic?" At this point, he looked at me as if I were an idiot and explained that nobody had to tell him about the clinic because everyone knew that Sheppard Pratt had always had an outpatient clinic, and that *he* ought to know because he had come here 30 years ago to get his two sessions of hypotherapy from Dr. Wooley. And now, he explained patiently, all he wanted was two more sessions.

Although my narcissism has never been the same since, I figured that at least we had the College Program, the General Hospital and the Training School for Boys Programs still going for us. These, at least, were still new under the sun. And then, last night Dr. Ives Hendrick told us that one of the first things that Dr. Harry Stack Sullivan did was to send him out to the Maryland Training School for Boys for half a day every week.

So that was another innovation down, leaving the College and the General Hospital Programs still to go. However, by now, I am completely convinced that before these meetings are over some alumnus will come up and fondly reminisce about how much fun it was to go every Tuesday afternoon to Towson State College and work with the students, and how nice it was on Friday to work in the emergency room of some long-forgotten general hospital that used to stand in the north pasture until it was burned down by gypsies in 1930—or something similar.

Anyway, for a few months there, we felt like innovators.

6

The "Dedicated Physician" in Psychotherapy and Psychoanalysis

HAROLD F. SEARLES, MD

Supervising and Training Analyst, The Washington Psychoanalytic Institute, Clinical Professor of Psychiatry, Georgetown University School of Medicine, Washington, Consultant in Psychotherapy, The Sheppard and Enoch Pratt Hospital, Towson

The dedication of the physician, when carried in conventional form into the practice of psychotherapy and psychoanalysis, serves as an unconscious defense in the therapist against the recognition of crucial aspects of the relationship to the patient. The patient derives from it both sadistic gratification and guilt at his feelings of hatefulness, unworthiness, and inability to give anything worthwhile to the "dedicated" therapist. Thus the therapist's "dedication" places the patient under great pressure with the end result that the latter is maintained in an infantilized state. When the therapist becomes more fully aware of his own feelings, he comes to see the patient as a real and separate person troubled by problems that are part of a genuinely outer reality, and not just a product of the therapist's own previously unrecognized hatred and infantile demands.

PSYCHIATRIC PATIENTS, AND ABOVE ALL schizophrenic patients, cause one to doubt one's capacity to love, and to feel that one's devotion is meaningless or, worse, malevolent. When I used to see a hebephrenic woman, with whom I had been working for ten years, walking about on the hospital grounds appearing vague, disheveled, bleakly unloved, I felt her to be a kind of living, ambulatory monument to my cruelty and neglect. Even though I had not forgotten that I had been subjected to something like two thousand hours of her reviling me, ignoring me, sexually tantalizing me, making heart-rendingly unanswerable appeals to me either mutely or in largely undecipherable words, and so on, I still

128

winced at the sight of her. It was as though the Methodist hell of my boyhood yawned widely for my thus-proved un-Christlike soul.

A year or two previously, on one of the rare days when she had her wits sufficiently about her to be considered able to come with me to my office, about 100 feet away, she stood in confused helplessness while an ostensibly kind, loving, gentle female aide, who (as I later came to realize) busily infantilized all the patients, was putting shoes on this woman's feet. I felt remorse because I did not feel at all like doing so—because I was feeling, at that moment, nothing toward the patient except impatience, contempt, and hatred.

My papers have chronicled my finding, to my mingled relief and self-deflation, how able schizophrenic patients are not merely to endure but to turn to therapeutic benefit one's expressions of deepeningly intense feelings of all kinds. But the events of my final year at Chestnut Lodge showed that I had underestimated to the last, nonetheless, these patients' strengths. I gave notice, one year in advance, of my intention to leave the Lodge; such notice was required by my contract, which in turn, of course, was based on clinical and staffing necessities. Regarding it feasible to go on working with no more than two of my six patients after I would leave there, I was now faced with the immensely difficult matter of which two, among six persons with whom I had been working intensively for years, I would go on seeing. With one of these persons, I had worked for nearly six years; with each of four, between ten and 11 years; and with one, for 13½ years.

My ambivalence toward each of these individuals, like his or her own toward me, of course, knew no bounds. I wanted utterly rid of the whole lot of them, yet felt almost unbearably anguished at the prospect of losing any one of them. A passage from my last staff presentation at the Lodge, just before I left, expresses something of what I had come to learn of the strength that each of these persons possessed:

> The one biggest lesson . . . I have learned in working with schizophrenic patients in my last year here has been to see how very tough they are. . . . I can say that I have, in this last year, burdened or battered, or what-not, each of these six patients with all the sarcasm, harshness, contempt, and just general resentment and reviling that I'm capable of and they've all survived it fine, see, just fine, and I have felt that I have just barely been operat-

ing in their league—just barely been qualifying to be in the major leagues. When I start this with Edna she is soon on the offensive again; she can take all I've got and she can go on for more.

Another way that I conceptualize it is, the work is so goddamned difficult that we cannot do it if we deny ourselves certain parts of our armamentarium. We can't do it with one hand tied behind our back. So this has been something memorable to me; this I'm going to keep using with patients. I am.

My experiences with colleagues over all these same years, as a supervisor or a consultant in their work with their schizophrenic patients, have shown me, similarly, with what toughness, tenacity, and sadistic virtuosity their patients tend to coerce these therapists into the ever-alluring role of the dedicated physician treating the supposedly weaker patient. Typically, to the extent that one feels bound by the traditional physician role, one feels wholly responsible for the course of the patient's illness, and believes it impermissible to experience any feelings toward the patient except kindly, attentive, long-suffering and helpful dedication. The psychiatric resident, in particular, relatively fresh from the dedicated-physician atmosphere of the medical school and general internship, is often genuinely unaware of feeling any hatred or even anger toward the patient who is daily ignoring or intimidating or castigating him, and unaware of how his very dedication, above all, makes him the prey of the patient's sadism. It has been many years since a young schizophrenic man revealed to me how much sadistic pleasure he was deriving from seeing a succession of dedicated therapists battering their heads bloody against the wall of his indifference, and I have never forgotten that.

In general, if the patient's illness is causing more suffering to the therapist than to the patient, then something is wrong. But it is not at all easy, technically, to become more comfortable than the patient. With many schizophrenic patients, one tends to feel like a butterfly, pinned squirmingly in their live-butterfly collection, without any reliable way of drawing blood from the pinner, the invulnerable patient. It is our omnipotent self-expectations that, more than anything else, pinion us and tend, as well, to stalemate or sever the therapeutic relationship. The obnoxiously behaving paranoid patient cannot help wondering what ulterior motives make us so concerned to *keep him in therapy;* instead of our becoming aware of our angrily wanting rid of him, we act out our repressed desires to reject him by manifesting an omnipotence-based, devouring, vampire-like devotion that understandably frightens him away from treatment. And the suicidal patient, who finds us so unable to be aware of the murderous feelings he fosters in us through his guilt-and-anxiety-producing threats of suicide, feels increasingly constricted, perhaps indeed to the point of suicide, by the therapist who, in reaction formation against his intensifying, unconscious wishes to kill the patient, hovers increasingly "protectively" about him, for whom he feels an omnipotence-based physicianly concern. Hence it is, paradoxically, the very physician most anxiously concerned to *keep the patient alive* who is tending most vigorously, at an unconscious level, to drive him to what has come to seem the only autonomous act left to him—suicide.

The therapist's functioning in the spirit of dedication that is the norm among physicians in other branches of medicine, represents in the practice of psychotherapy and psychoanalysis an unconscious defense against his seeing clearly many crucial aspects of both the patient and himself—for example, sadism. He does not see how much sadistic gratification the patient is deriving from his anguished, tormented, futile dedication. He does not realize that, as I overheard one chronically schizophrenic man confide to his therapist, "The pleasure I get in torturing you is the main reason I go on staying in this hospital." I had heard this therapist say that for many months he had never known, when he went into this man's room on the disturbed ward, whether to expect a blow or a kiss from the patient.

Further, the dedicated therapist does not see how much ambivalence the patient has concerning change, even change for the "better." He does not see that the patient has reached his present equilibrium only after years of thought and effort and the exercise of the best judgment of which he is capable. To the patient, change tends to mean a return to an intolerable preequilibrium state, and the imposition on him of the therapist's values, the therapist's personality, with no autonomy, no individuality, for him. He resents the therapist's presumption in assuming that the patient is pitiably eager to be rescued, and equally humiliatingly, that the intended help is all unidirectional, from therapist to patient.

A dozen years ago, I reached the conviction that it is folly to set out to rescue the patient from the dragon of schizophrenia: the patient is both the maiden in the dragon's grip and the dragon itself. The dragon is the patient's resistance to becoming "sane" —resistance that shows itself as a tenacious and savage hostility to the therapist's efforts.

The heart of this resistance springs from the fact that, since early childhood, the patient's own *raison d'être* has been as a therapist, originally to the parent whose unwhole integration he, the child, was called upon to complement, in a pathologic and unnaturally prolonged symbiosis. He was given over to this therapeutic dedication, as a small child, for the most altruistic of reasons—he lived in order to make mother (or father) whole—as well as for reasons of his own self-interest, so that he would have a whole parent with whom to identify, for the sake of his own maturation. But he failed in his therapeutic dedication; and, more hurtfully, his dedication was not even recognized by the parent, who incessantly hurt, disparaged, and rejected him. Now, as an adult schizophrenic patient in treatment, he takes vengeance on this rival, "official" therapist of his, and causes his therapist to feel as anguished, futile, and worthless or malevolent an intended healer as he had been made to feel by his mother or father. Only insofar as the therapist becomes able to see and respond to the patient's genuinely therapeutic striving toward him and, earlier, toward the parents, will the patient himself be receptive to therapy. Among my feelings during the final year at Chestnut Lodge was, prominently, grief at various of my patients' having refused to identify sufficiently with my healthier aspects and, by the same token, at my own having failed to help them do so. I surmise that such grief is of a piece with the patient's own repressed grief, stemming from early childhood, at proving unable to save the sick parent through encouraging him to identify with the healthier aspects of the patient as a growing child.

We therapists tend to feel frightened away from seeing how concerned our patients are to help us, partly for the reason that the transference-distortions, in which this therapeutic striving of theirs is couched, are very great. That is, our patient tends to see us as being not merely somewhat depressed today, but as being his deeply, suicidally despondent father; or he perceives us as being not merely somewhat scatterbrained today, but as being his insane, hopelessly fragmented mother.

Patients' specific therapeutic aims, and their individual techniques in pursuing those aims, are manifold. As examples, various of my patients have rescued me from periods of withdrawal and depression by presenting themselves as being in such urgent need of rescue that I have felt it necessary to bestir myself, come out of myself, and thus cast off the chains of my depression in order to save them. Others, by presenting themselves as being infuriatingly, outrageously undisciplined, have eventually "made a man of" me—by impelling me into becoming a stern disciplinarian, have made me into the kind of man that they had been unable to make their wishy-washy father into.

Their therapeutic techniques are outwardly so brutal that the therapeutic intent is seen only in the result. One apathetic, dilapidated hebephrenic patient of mine received considerable therapeutic benefit from a fellow patient, newly come to the ward but, like him, a veteran of several years in mental hospitals, who repeatedly, throughout the day, gave my patient a vigorous and unexpected kick in the behind. From what I could see, this was the first time in years a fellow patient had shown any real interest in him, and my patient as a result emerged appreciably from his state of apathy and hopelessness.

As for the many crucial aspects of himself in relation to the patient, against which the therapist is unconsciously defending himself with his physicianly dedication, I have already touched on some. He is unaware of how much he is enjoying his tormenting the patient with his dedication, of which the patient, who feels himself to be hateful and incapable of giving anything worthwhile to any one, feels so unworthy. He is unaware, similarly, of how much scorn his own "dedication" is expressing. I asked a female colleague, who was describing her work, a very actively dedicated and ostensibly maternally loving work with a deeply regressed woman, how much ego she felt the patient to have. The therapist replied, as though this were obvious, "None." Such unconscious scorn for the patient—for the patient's own strength and for his ability to reach out, himself, for help from the therapist without the therapist's having constantly to keep pushing the help at him—seems to me to betray much self-contempt on the part of the therapist. If the therapist is convinced that he himself is a worthwhile person, with something useful to give—with something, that is, that this fellow human being, the patient, can be relied on to discern and to admire and want—he will not need to try, anxiously and incessantly, to persuade the patient to accept his help.

Further, the "dedicated" therapist, who feels under such intense pressure to cure the patient, goes on oblivious of his placing, through his dedication, equally great pressure on the patient. I can offer here a vignette from my own work. A paranoid schizophrenic woman whom I have been treating for years has come, in recent months, to spend many sessions wet-eyed, describing in verbose detail her life-experience, current and past, in terms that imply that there is an ocean of grief in her, but never with any frank outpouring of tears. Finally, at the end of one such session, I confided to her, with mixed feelings of guilt and exasperation, that at the end of such an hour as this, as many times before: "You always make me feel remiss in not having said or done something that would enable you to weep." To my surprise, she instantly responded with something that evidently had been on her mind for many sessions: "And *you* always make *me* feel remiss for not weeping."

The supervision of other therapists gives one a chance to see these things more objectively and, of course, with less harsh narcissistic injury to oneself. Specifically, one can clearly feel how sadistic are the demands on oneself, week after week, of the so-dedicated therapist who is agonizedly eager to cure his patient. One such therapist, chronically depressed and long-suffering about the work with his patient but chronically "dedicated" to the latter, would tell me, week after week, of his patient's asking him, "What do I do? What's the right thing to do?" He himself was passing along to me much this same kind of draining and unanswerable demand by implicitly asking me, throughout each supervisory session, "Doc, what do I do to relieve my suffering at the hands of this patient who is crucifying me?"

Our "dedicated physician" way of relating to the patient serves not only to act out our sadism toward him but also to express our unconscious determination to maintain the status quo—to preserve the patient's present, immature level of ego-functioning in order to ensure the inflow of deniedly-cherished supplies from him. Thus, the loosening of the stalemate requires that the therapist become aware of not only his sadism and other negative feelings toward the patient but also his cherishing what the latter has been providing him.

In other words, an intensely pressuring, dedicated therapeutic zeal denotes an unconscious determination, on the part of the therapist, to protect and preserve, for reasons of his own psychic economy, the patient's present level of psychotic or neurotic ego-functioning, because of various narcissistic and infantile gratifications that the therapist is receiving from the patient, who represents at one level a transference-mother who is feeding him, and because the patient's illness serves to shield the therapist from seeing clearly his own illness.

So, unconsciously, the therapist is bent on maintaining the patient in an infantilized state, and is opposing that very individuation and maturation to which, at a conscious level, he is genuinely dedicated. I, for one, tend dedicatedly to remain immersed in a rescue-effort toward the "fragile" patient, in order to avoid seeing him or her as being stronger, or potentially stronger, than myself. For example, one hebephrenic woman, from whose incredibly low levels of ego-functioning I derived many fascinating data about the schizophrenic patient's subjectively "prehuman" identity (data included in my monograph on the nonhuman environment), finally told me, in vigorous protest, "I can't stay down forever!" This woman would evidence, from time to time over the years of our work, remarkable forward surges in her ego-functioning, and unfailingly I would find that my rejoicing in this development was outweighed by an upsurge of my feeling inadequate. I had been feeling despair at how grievously ill she was; but now I would find her manifesting an appearance of blooming physical health that made me feel old and jaded, and I would be reminded, ruefully, too, that she was physically taller than I. In the same process, she would reveal a kind of effortless *savoir faire,* in matters both interpersonal and cultural, traceable to an upbringing far richer in social and cultural "advantages" than my own. In short, I would feel her to be an all-around hopelessly larger person than myself. Then, as if quickly detecting that I still couldn't take it, she would soon be, again, her deeply fragmented, "hopelessly ill" hebephrenic self, and I was once more in my comfortable role of the long-suffering Christ trying to heal this wounded bird.

Even more embarrassingly, I found my feelings toward another long-schizophrenic woman oscillating, often session by session for months on end, from my viewing her as a hopelessly confused mental patient who, clearly incurably ill, would undoubtedly be spending the rest of her life in psychiatric hospitals, to my viewing her as a predominantly well, wonderfully warm, intelligent, and witty woman for whom I felt greatly tempted to give up every one and everything else in my life, but who, I had anguishedly to realize, recurrently, could never practicably be mine. At this point, incidentally, it should be abundantly clear that, among the needs for which the "dedicated" therapist is obtaining gratification are his masochistic needs.

The more deeply one examines the psychodynamics of the dedicated-physician therapist who is unconsciously devoted to preserving the status quo, one finds that he holds, at an unconscious level, split images, one an idealized image and the other a diabolized image, of himself and of the patient as well, and that he is dedicated, unconsciously but tenaciously, to preserving these split images and preventing their coalescence, with the leaven of reality, into realistic images of himself and of the patient as two fellow human beings, each possessing both strengths and limitations on his strengths, each capable of hating *and* loving.

As a function of his unconscious effort to preserve these split images, the therapist represses the ingredients of his diabolized self-image—his hatred, his rejectingness, his subjectively nonhuman unfeelingness, and so on—and projects these on the patient. At the same time that he is placing intense though unwitting demands on the patient to emerge in such a healthy way as will enable the therapist to realize his idealized self-image as an all-loving and omnipotent healer, he is unconsciously holding at a safe distance, or driving progressively deeper into autism, this patient who personifies the diabolized, unacceptable, and therefore vigorously projected aspects of his own self-image. Thus the therapist's dedication becomes, from this vantage point, an anxious, deeply ambivalent effort both to make contact with and to keep safely at a distance the projected components of his *self*.

To describe this a bit further. How well it serves the therapist's unconscious rejectingness for the patient to become progressively withdrawn. Consciously, he is dedicated to making contact with the patient and helping him to join him in the "real world"; unconsciously, he wants rid of the disappointing, frightening, and otherwise unsatisfactory patient—the patient who by any standards is so, and all the more by reason of the therapist's unconscious image of him as presently diabolical, no matter how much the therapist clings also to the unconscious hope that the patient may one day fit an ideal image. In still other terms, the therapist is trying consciously to help the withdrawn patient to materialize, while unconsciously he wants to make him disappear. In proportion as the patient becomes able to evidence love, the therapist's projected image of himself as diabolical comes home to roost, and he tends to perceive himself as subhumanly bad, malevolently obstructing the full liberation of the patient's supposedly suprahumanly good self. What makes this so formidable a difficulty, in therapy, is not so much that the therapist is unadulteratedly neurotic, but rather that the chronically schizophrenic patient contributes to the maintenance of these processes of splitting a degree of intensity and tenacity of which the therapist's own stake in the matter is a relatively small sample. But it is the therapist's own dawning recognition of his "countertransference"—his own contribution to these stalemating processes—that provides the best handle for his effecting a change in the therapeutic relationship; that is why I dwell here on the therapist's contribution to the difficulties.

We tend, thus, to give the patient to feel both idealized and diabolized by us, with a hopelessly unbridgeable gulf between these two so-different creatures we are calling on him to be toward us. At the same time that we are unwittingly calling on him to fulfill our diabolized image of him, we are unconsciously looking to him to provide our life with its central meaning, to give us a *raison d'être*, to make real our idealized self-image. I want to emphasize that it is no pernicious thing *consciously* to regard the patient as supremely important and meaningful to oneself. For us consciously so to relate to him can only enhance his self-esteem and help him to become whole. The pernicious thing is that we repress both our idealized image and our diabolized image of him, hide both from ourself and at the same time act out both these toward him, by inappropriately employing, in psychotherapy and psychoanalysis, the traditional dedicated-physician-treating-his-patient approach that, however conventionally accepted in the practice of medicine generally, congeals and reinforces the wall between patient and doctor when we employ it in this field.

Paradoxically, the withdrawn patient is likely to be identifying with the very therapist who is consciously devoted to a diligent and even desperate attempt to help him emerge from the withdrawal, but many of whose feelings are actually withdrawn from his conscious attitudes toward the patient. That is, the patient, in seeking the isolation of the seclusion room, may well be identifying with those increments of the therapist that are secluded from access to the therapist's conscious ways of viewing and relating to the patient. This is one variety of what I have termed, in an earlier writing, delusional identification, on the patient's part, with his therapist. In general, these are instances in which the most tenacious, treatment-resistant aspects of the patient's craziness are found based on his exaggerated and distorted identifications with real but unconscious aspects of the therapist's own personality and ways of functioning in the treatment-relationship.

In discussing now the phenomena marking the resolution of these dedicated-physician stalemates—phenomena of which I have already hinted—I have in mind the form this resolution takes in one's work with the schizophrenic patient on the one hand, and with the depressed patient on the other; but there are many patients, of course, who show prominently both these varieties of psychopathology.

In any case, as the therapist becomes aware of the whole gamut of his feelings toward the patient, he comes to see that the patient is a real and separate person, afflicted with an illness that is also a part of genuinely outer reality for the therapist, rather than its being the product of the therapist's heretofore repressed, subjectively omnipotent hatred and infantile demands.

As we become free from our previous compulsive "dedication" and able now with our new objectivity to view the patient and our relationship with him, we no longer assume a wholehearted, dedicated interest on our part as a *given* in the situation, and can notice in our interest toward him fluctuations, often fostered by him, of much transference-significance. For example, I have seen that, with various of my patients, just as we get to working closely and most constructively together, the patient will do something (such as making a last-minute, inconsiderate and impersonal cancellation of a session) that cools my interest in him, thus revealing to me his fear of closeness with me, his fear of my strong, sustained and deepening interest in him, which I would not have detected had I gone on holding myself totally responsible for maintaining an unflagging interest in helping him—had I gone on feeling guilty whenever I found myself not interested in him and not caring whether he might elect to continue with our work. This is but an example of how, in analytic terms, a therapist's physicianly, compulsive "dedication" interferes with the kind of free-floating objectivity that is so necessary an ingredient of the analyst's effective functioning.

As our previous, compulsive dedication loosens its grip on us, we become aware—lo and behold—of a keen esthetic appreciation of that very illness in the patient which heretofore we have felt so desperately and guiltily responsible for curing. Several years ago, I found myself having to face the fact that I seemed to find much more fascinating the schizophrenic, then the more conventional and healthier, aspects of my patients' functioning. At first, I felt deeply troubled at this discovery, for I believed that it must mean that I am dedicated more to the causation and preservation of severe and exotic illness than to the fostering of health in my patients. But then I began to see that my preference was not so unnatural, after all. Keeping in mind the point I made earlier—that the schizophrenic patient is not only the maiden in the dragon's grip but the dragon also—let me ask you which of these you find more fascinating: the relatively pallid and conventional lady, or the exotic and colorful dragon?

I have been deeply reassured to find, as time has gone on, that this very esthetic appreciation is a form of scientific interest that, in contrast to my earlier anguished therapeutic dedication, enables me to be of maximal use to the patient. For example, I used to feel, for years, desperately and urgently concerned to relieve the indescribably severe confusion of one of my chronically schizophrenic patients, and it was with guilt bordering on self-loathing that I began to realize that I was actually fascinated by the vivid, intricate, so-unconventional nature of her confusion itself. At first, my interest in this felt unclean, perverse, unworthy of any physician; but gradually I came to feel that I was facing a genuine work of creative art, which is, as I now clearly see, the product of the highest forms of the patient's intelligence and creative originality. As for her, she shows every evidence of finding much more useful my appreciative, unanxious and unguilty studying of her confused verbalizations, than she used to find my desperate attempts somehow to shut them off.

Along with such esthetic-scientific interest, one comes to feel, as one becomes freer from omnipotent guilt about the patient and his illness, companion gratifications in the realm of humor and playfulness—all necessary ingredients of the phase of the mutually enjoyable therapeutic symbiosis that I have described in a number of writings. Time after time, I have found that the patient benefits most from our sharing humorous, playful moments together. When I can leave off my deadly serious dedication, and be amused at the patient's craziness, he can come to laugh with warm and loving amusement at the delightfully crazy foibles of his mother, whom he had been desperately dedicated, heretofore, to curing, at

Saint George and the Dragon
PAOLO UCCELLO (c. 1396-1475)
Courtesy of the National Gallery, London

an introjected level, in his own tragic craziness. When one is working in this new spirit with the patient, one is very close to him,
openly showing how much one likes and enjoys being with him.
His formerly maddening symptoms are now only part of the background music in an atmosphere of contentment.

As the therapist becomes aware of how much gratification the
illness is providing to him as well as to the patient, he becomes free
of his infantile omnipotence-based guilty feeling of *having to cure*
the patient. The patient genuinely is faced now, not simply at one
crucial juncture but ongoingly, session after session, with the
choice whether he himself wishes to cling to the gratifications of
remaining ill or to accept the therapist's *also*-offered assistance in
becoming a healthy adult.

Conclusion

Briefly, three points. First, it seems impossible—and perhaps it
would be untherapeutic if it were possible—for a therapist to have
at the beginning of his work with any one patient, and to maintain
throughout the treatment, a realistic as opposed to an omnipotence-based feeling of dedication. It would be unclinical to postulate that there is *one* most therapeutic attitude as regards dedication that the therapist should have at the beginning of the therapy
and maintain throughout it, beyond his dedicating himself as fully
as possible to becoming aware of whatever thoughts and feelings
are being called forth, in the treatment process, in himself as well
as in the patient. It seems inescapable that we shall go through
torments of feeling omnipotently responsible for each of our patients, that we shall repress our sadism and project it on the patient, that we will come to develop split images of ourself and of
the patient, and so on; and it may well be that our becoming thus
enmeshed, for a time, in the patient's illness is necessary to the
therapeutic process. But I suggest that the considerations discussed
here will facilitate our going through this evolution and emerging
to a more realistic experience of ourself in relation to the patient.
I suggest, in other words, that these considerations will help us to
avert, or at least to shorten, such covertly sadomasochistic stalemates as are familiar clinical experiences to all of us.

Second, we see that the kind of therapist-devotion characteristic
of such stalemated situations is a genuinely "selfless" devotion, but
selfless in a sense that is, in the long run, precisely   antithera-

peutic. That is, so many of the therapist's own unconscious ingredients are being projected onto the patient that he is in a real sense
selflessly submerged in the patient's narcissism. In this sense, the
therapist is deriving the unconscious gratification of functioning
without the responsibility for having a self and thus, paradoxically, in his "selflessly dedicated" functioning is burdening the
patient with a total responsibility for the whole relationship. Such
"devotion", which temporarily supports the patient's narcissistic
world-self, inevitably must be revealed one day as a lie. This disil-
lusioning discovery, now, that the therapist after all is a separate
person with a self and a self-interest of his own, after the patient
has been led for so long to assume otherwise, will repeat for the
patient his bitter childhood experience that, as one schizophrenic
woman put it, "People are interested only in themselves," and as a
borderline schizophrenic man phrased it, "Kidding your children
for 20 years that you love them and want them—this is what I'm
bitter about, I guess; Mother has *pretended* that she put me first,
and it's just been her little game. It's not been true—she's more
interested in herself, in her neurosis. . . ."

The paranoid individual is especially prone to assuming that if
the therapist proves not to be wholeheartedly devoted to his welfare, then the therapist must be bent on sabotaging and destroying
him. This assumption seems referable to the patient's experiences
as a child, in which the parents maintained a "wholeheartedly
devoted" demeanor toward him, in a reaction-formation against
their largely unconscious, more sinister feelings toward him—their
hostility toward him, their wishes to be free of him. Hence he will
remain suspicious, and with good reason, if we endeavor to sub-
merge, from the beginning of his treatment, our self-interest in his
"welfare".

Third, in earlier papers [1] I have described the therapeutic
symbiosis, which implies a degree of selflessness on the part of
therapist as well as patient, as marking the most essential aspect of
the treatment. But this stands in the most direct contrast to the
kind of "dedicated-physician selflessness" that this paper is questioning. Where the latter is a defense against hatred and other
"negative" emotions, this former kind of merging between patient
and therapist can occur only after all emotions, of whatever variety
and in either participant, have become so unthreatening that these
need no longer be defended against by the maintenance of a
"self," a structure which, in light of the processes at work in this

stage of the threatment-evolution, could serve only as a hindrance to the therapeutic forces that are streaming toward new and deeper patterns of individuation for both patient and therapist, patterns at this point unpredictable and therefore all the more exciting and fulfilling.

REFERENCE

1. Searles, H. F.: Collected Papers on Schizophrenia and Related Subjects, London, Hogarth Press and The Institute of Psycho-Analysis; New York, Internat Univ Press, 1965.

Discussion

ALEXANDER REID MARTIN, MD, DPM

*Honorary Member of the Staff of The Sheppard and Enoch
Pratt Hospital, Towson, Maryland*

COMING BACK, I RECALL *You Can't Go Home Again* by Thomas Wolfe, one of whose problems was that he couldn't go home again, back to his roots and his beginnings. After many years' absence, I am deeply thankful that I am able to come back to Sheppard Pratt. I cannot say "Back to these hallowed halls," because I was never in this hall before; I can say "Back to these hallowed hills and fields, and to the hallowed A and B Buildings."

Before I left Glasgow, I did research on the use of tryparsamide in general paralysis, which was published in the British *Lancet* in 1926. This was Neurological Psychiatry. My next printed appearance was in the *Quarterly Bulletin* of the Maryland School for Boys, in 1928. There, thanks to Ross Chapman and Harry Stack Sullivan, I was graduated to Social Psychiatry, along with Ives Hendrick.

Dr. Searles's chapter focuses on an area of profound significance to psychotherapy, where considerable misunderstanding, misdirection, and misinterpretation can occur—the concept of dedication, always part of our whole approach in medicine and therapy. Surely, in Moses Sheppard's approach dedication was the fundamental element. But let me sound a strong warning: we have to proceed carefully. I am sure that you all would agree that what we have to avoid is compulsive dedication, compulsive involvement with our patient, and the compulsive need to reassure that goes along with it. In our early days of therapy, we all went through a period of compulsive dedication, and we know that the compulsive need to reassure assails all young psychoanalysts.

At Sheppard Pratt, I became dedicated to the study of schizophrenia. When I went to Paul Schilder for my beginning analysis,

144

I decided I would dedicate my life to this area of psychiatry. Then, when I came to Karen Horney for psychoanalysis in New York, I learned that my dedication was compulsive: not inner-directed but other-directed, neurotically motivated and exploitive, primarily to satisfy something in myself.

The nature of our dedication, its quality, whether inner-directed or other-directed, has many determinants, but much depends on our orientation and our basic premises. For instance, we have to realize that we are not a healing profession, we are a treating profession. Laennec said, "I treat my patients, God cures them." I was glad to hear Dr. McLaughlin yesterday speak of orienting ourselves to a health concept rather than a disease concept. On this premise, we would primarily orient ourselves towards helping nature—that is, helping our patient to find out what *his* nature is doing, and then aligning ourselves with it. "Nature does nothing in vain," wrote Sir Thomas Browne in *Religio Medici.* Another helpful basis for our therapeutic orientation, endorsed by the World Health Organization, is the unitary concept of health and disease as degrees or modalities of adaptation. I mention these basic orientations because they may help to lead us away from reactive compulsive dedication towards active inner-directed dedication.

As human beings are inclined to do, we turn compulsive dedication into a virtue. Such a dedicated psychiatrist is easily seduced by the patient into playing God. Once the patient maneuvers you into playing this role and usurping his authority, he will covertly start to knock you down, defeat you and outwit you. I've had more than one patient say to me, when this particular neurotic maneuver was coming to the surface: "I was getting my biggest feeling of triumph out of seeing you fail. I want to be your biggest failure." The kind of authority you are seduced into playing is the *quid pro quo,* venal, corruptive authority, the authority to be bargained with, and that totally subscribes to *lex talionis,* an eye for an eye, a tooth for a tooth.

Compulsive dedication, with its compulsive need to reassure, also sets the stage for directive rather than nondirective therapy. Directive or nondirective therapy, a great area of controversy today, needs to be carefully defined. In my practice, I am inclined towards being nondirective. By this, I mean that I will use my authority when I consider it helpful, but that I will never usurp the patient's authority or encroach on his autonomy so far as I can help. So often we overlook the fact that the patient who insists or infers that we are permissive is placing us in an authoritative role. If we maintain this role, then we perpetuate morbid dependency.

Recapitulating, our dedication should be gracious and inner-directed, a dedication free and unmerited. I would say: dedicate yourself to an ideology of health rather than an ideology of disease, to Hygeia, Goddess of Health, and only secondarily to Aesculapius, God of Medicine. We forget how strongly we are oriented to pathology. Our dedication should be to the whole patient, as a static pattern in space as well as a dynamic pattern in time. In this dedication, we address ourselves to the whole patient and not only to his articulate periphery; we address ourselves to the manifest and the latent content, and we take the patient and what he says literally and figuratively. Above all, we respect the patient's own language and we use it as much as possible. With such active dedication, the patient becomes imbued with our respect for his totality and our respect for his unconscious, subconscious and conscious, and this leads to greater respect for himself and hence to a stronger ego.

Discussion

Russell R. Monroe, MD

Professor of Psychiatry, Director of Graduate Training, The Psychiatric Institute, University of Maryland School of Medicine, Baltimore

Doctor Searles's exposition pleases me, because I believe that the best way to convey the art of psychotherapy is through personal anecdotal material. This can be painful, for it reveals as much about the therapist as about the therapeutic process. But I appreciate Dr. Searles's candor, and I know that his is a good chapter because it stirred in me considerable introspection and retrospection, at a time I could ill afford such luxury.

I shall offer, rather than a critique, an addendum, because I have come to many of the same conclusions and have had many similar experiences, though in a completely different setting. My professional experience has been limited to outpatient insight psychotherapy or psychoanalysis with patients who, if labeled, would be called neurotic or borderline; a number manifested impulsivity and would be called "acter outers."

My interest was supposedly motivated by a scientific predilection rather than any personal masochism, although at times I wonder. While my work was going on, I was at the same time a full-time teacher associated with medical schools and general hospitals. But never less than one-third nor more than one-half of my time was devoted to private patients.

For the first ten years of my practice, I was a super- "dedicated physician." I lived a schizophrenic existence; with some patients, I was the ambiguous figure behind the couch, hopefully reflecting, in an undistorted way, the transference neuroses. With others, I was the dedicated physician. If my patient had taken an overdose of barbiturates, I was there pumping out her stomach. If there was any question of a brain lesion, I was there with a pin and a reflex hammer, doing a neurologic examination. I made home visits dur-

147

ing crises; I had a little black bag and it was filled with a stethoscope, a blood pressure cuff and injectable amytal. This was considerably reinforced in my setting, because my colleagues would throw their arms around my shoulders and say, "Well, we've finally found a real psychiatrist—one who acts like a doctor." I suspect that this was a reaction formation because my original professional goals had been to become a laboratory scientist and teacher, but halfway through medical school it became the better part of valor to become a physician because World War II came along. As my professional career evolved, I assumed more and more administrative responsibilities, teaching obligations became heavier, and my laboratory grew and demanded a lot of my time.

Now in such a situation, one's patients become less important to him. But rather than having a bad effect on my relationships with my patients and the therapeutic process, this fact had a good effect. There was a period of some anguish. Because I was held in other commitments, I was often late for appointments. At times, a long-winded meeting in the dean's office meant that I had to call my secretary to cancel an appointment, even though the patient was already in my office. Because I traveled more, therapy was interrupted often at times inappropriate for the patient. Of course, my patients reviled me, degraded me, and accused me of failing in my professional responsibilities, and even suggested that I was acting unethically. I took them seriously, and became convinced that perhaps I was.

And so I made a decision that as soon as I could complete the treatment of the patients I was then seeing, I would give up treatment and do only consultations. I thought in the meantime that what I will have to do is to be rather candid with my patients. So, right in the middle of the therapeutic process, I would say, "I'll have to cancel your appointments next week. I'm sorry. It's an exam week, and I'm going to be grading papers all week." Or, if an emergency came up in the evening, even when it was a realistic one not just a manipulation, and the patient wanted to talk with me on the 'phone, or I felt maybe an emergency appointment was justified, I would say, "I'm awfully sorry. I agree with you. I think it would be good if we could get together and talk about this, but we will have to postpone it until our regular session. I'm entertaining a visiting dignitary tonight." And so on.

What surprised me was that my patients seemed to be responding to this in a very positive way. As I thought about it, their treatment seemed to be accelerated or facilitated rather than slowed. I knew that there is great danger of personal rationalization when one gets in a situation like this, so I tried to work this out in my own mind. Perhaps to relieve some of my own guilt, I began openly to redefine my role with the patients. What I tried to define, both in words and actions, was that I was not their doctor and that they were not my patients. In fact, I became quite insistent that I did not consider them sick. Unhappy, or inefficient, or aimlessly drifting, yes; sick, no. And I tried to use a model in my own mind and to convey this to the patient, that I was more like the piano teacher and they more like the pupil than the usual doctor-patient model. For instance, if a patient of mine had said or made a statement similar to that of the patient whom Dr. Searles described at the end of his chapter—"If they want to stay sick and screwed up it is their business, and their choice, but it's not mine" —I might have stepped in and said something like: "Yes, and if you want to stay sick and screwed up, that's your business and your choice. And as long as it's your choice, it's also mine."

As might be expected, there is no dramatic change in the patient's behavior when one states these things as a mere fact. They still go on with all of their unrealistic expectations of the omnipotent doctor who will give them aid without any particular effort on their own part. And so I think that one has to back up these kinds of stated attitudes with one's behavior, and what helped most was this increasing candor with the patient. If they call up, just tell them no, or that it might be very valuable to get together and talk, or that you are sorry that you might have to interrupt treatments for the next two weeks while you go on a trip, but this is your obligation. You have to do this. You have obligations other than treating them.

This brings up what obligations they have to you. I think that Dr. Searles has succinctly described how the patients feel in terms of what obligations they have to the doctor. I remembered that once I blurted out, "Look, you don't owe me anything except your fee!" I immediately felt that this was a rather cruel thing to say to the patient and was quite surprised to see how relieved the patient was. I am sure many of you have had this kind of experience, too. But, inevitably, there comes a point in therapy when the patients demand this dedicated physician, and then I find myself in the position of having to say to them: "Now, look, I think I can help you in the way I am doing it, but if you don't think so, if you think you need this other kind of physician, then I will help you find one." And quite often they take me up.

As I look around the audience, in fact, I see several doctors who have seen irate patients of mine, and I want to thank you, and add that it's probably to a great extent due to your delicate handling of the situations that most of the referrals come back to finish their therapy with me.

I am concerned about how much this is a rationalization, but Dr. Searles gave me a counterrationalization. After all, maybe my behavior is realistic and I am escaping from this neurotic sadomasochistic involvement with my patients. Of course, you still must have a true commitment to your patients. I think, though, that it is easier to have a true commitment to them if you are not all-encompassingly involved with the rescue fantasy. The patients really feel, in this situation, I think, an overwhelming sense of responsibility. Who is responsible for their change? They are! It helps them to emancipate themselves from this unending involvement with the therapy and with the therapeutic situation as an end in itself rather than a means to an end. In fact, the highest compliment that I have had in a long time was from a patient who was terminated several months ago. One of his final benedictions was this:

> "For at least 30 of the 36 months we have been working together, I've hated your guts. Now that treatment is terminating, I don't know whether I'm well or not. I'm not even sure I'm happier, but life seems much more exciting and worth living. You know, I don't even know whether you helped me much, or whether I might have done the same thing for myself alone. But as I look back, I somehow feel grateful to you and the way you handled my therapy."

I hasten to add that I think it is a lot easier for me, in my setting, perhaps with my delayed identity crisis, to make the shift from the physician to the teacher, because I work with a very select group of patients, and I do consciously select them. I am looking for the relatively healthy, certainly very healthy compared to the type of patients that Dr. Searles was describing. I am sure that it is easier for me to do this than it is for him. I do not know whether I should have treated the schizophrenic patients who were or had been hospitalized for a long period of time. I am not sure I would have had the courage to do this, as Dr. Searles did.

7

Behavior and Inner Experience
Parallels and Contradictions in the Appraisal of Treatment

SAMUEL NOVEY, MD

Director of Training, The Sheppard and Enoch Pratt Hospital, Towson, Maryland, Associate Professor of Psychiatry, The Johns Hopkins University School of Medicine, Baltimore

The goals of treatment of certain neurotic patients seen in private practice are contrasted with those in the psychoses and in a short-term treatment project involving neurotic patients from the lowest socioeconomic levels. The results with the patients in private practice are appraised according to experience in living; behavioral patterns are not the primary point of reference.

In the psychoses and in the research project at Johns Hopkins, the goals of treatment are oriented towards experiments in living that will modify repetitive attitudes and behavior. Objective appraisal becomes enormously more difficult when the emphasis is on the patient's private experience rather than strictly behavioral considerations. Although suffering from inhibition in the more mundane activities of living deserves attention, so does suffering from inhibition in emotional experience.

THE MEANS OF APPRAISING THE RESULTS of different modes of treatment of the emotional disorders has always been a tantalizing problem, regardless of the degree of mildness or severity of the disorder under consideration or of the type of treatment employed, from the briefest supportive therapy to the most extensive psychoanalysis. Some of the central problems intrinsic to such appraisals are the subject of this chapter.

The differences between measuring the results of treatment on the basis of inner experience in living rather than social performance will be the primary point of reference. Sometimes maximal self-realization and maximal social performance do coincide, and insofar as they do there is no problem. Many moralistically oriented groups believe that such correlation is inevitable and is a kind of natural law. This formulation is more wish than fact, however, and some of the ways in which its limitations bear on our attempts to evaluate treatment warrant elaboration. In the broadest sense, some contrasts will be drawn between the goals of treatment in the psychoses in general and in a particular group of the neuroses. The neurotic patients are those seen in many psychiatric and psychoanalytic private practices—essentially all from the higher socioeconomic group. To clarify this issue further, the treatment goals in a short-term treatment project involving neurotic patients of the lowest socioeconomic group are contrasted with those of the private-practice patients. These comparisons will illustrate the relevance of behavioral as contrasted to experiential frames of reference in the appraisal of treatment.

Patients hospitalized with psychoses represent a group of people with emotional disorders that are evidenced, more often than not, by the grossest aberrations of *behavioral patterns*. Considering the two major classes of functional psychoses, there is a general consensus that the schizophrenic psychoses are primarily disorders of the thought processes while the manic depressive psychoses are primarily disorders of affect. No special exception to this is taken when it is emphasized that, in their florid state at least, both are marked by gross behavioral deviations from the cultural norm, and that this constitutes the basic reason for care within the hospital. One need hardly add that this is even more blatantly evident in such increasingly common causes of hospitalization as alcoholism.

In the event that the psychotic patient improves, he follows a more *socially appropriate* mode of behavior, and the matter of his discharge from the hospital is determined primarily by the estimate of whether such socially appropriate behavior could be sustaining in quality. An important index of this is obtained when the patient is again exposed to certain extrahospital pressures, felt to be contributory if not primary causes of the prior disorganization of behavior. This affords the opportunity to observe whether the patient will again present regressive behavioral patterns or not. Accordingly, as the patient improves in his ability to behave in a socially appropriate way, with the help of drugs, milieu, psychotherapy or the natural process of the illness, he is encouraged to make brief visits away from the hospital. By means of visits with parents or spouse, or of interaction in other social situations, his behavior is appraised in the face of these stresses. Socially acceptable behavior is a primary measure of improvement in the course of the illness.

In some classes of psychoses, at least, and particularly as the acute behavioral aberrations subside, more or less extensive considerations may be entered into between patient and therapist concerning the causes of the breakdown of social performance. Likely, some considerations will also be engaged in of other modes, both experiential and behavioral, of coping with heretofore intolerable external and internal stresses. Particularly in the schizophrenic patient, recovery—with residual difficulties in the way of certain rigidities of character and of performance, and with some flattening of affect—is not in itself a measure of the lack of a successful result. In fact, it may well be that these very rigidities and limitations of affectivity may be necessary conditions for the maintenance of the state of improvement and that tampering with them in the hope of a "better result" may be foolhardy and may precipitate a reemergence of the florid schizophrenic state. It is a common experience that a good many of these patients have sufficient awareness or inner sense of this fact to protect both themselves and the too ardent therapist against such overenthusiasm, even by disrupting treatment if this becomes necessary.

The emphasis in the description above is on *behavioral* modes as the primary point of reference in the appraisal of the results of treatment. This is not said in criticism but as an often necessary, even crucial orientation for both the individual and the society. As suggested, even the verbal exploration of motivating factors in the illness must often wait on the patient's capacity to verbalize in a more or less coherent fashion—it being in itself a behavioral modality, in one sense of the word at least. There are a number of theoretical formulations that are useful in attempting to understand and to treat the psychoses. Some typical examples of these are the theories having to do with reality testing, object relationships, modes of internalization, and the nature of object representations. These conceptualizations play an important role in outlining the treatment strategy in any given case. Cognizance of these factors influence the outcome of treatment. Despite this, however, the focal point in appraising the result of treatment in the psychoses is behavioral. Man "is what he does" in this frame of reference, and the capacity to behave in certain particular ways and not in other ways is taken as a prime measure of the individual.

If attention is directed from the psychoses—where the *primary* goal, in therapy at least, is on behavioral aberration and its therapeutic modification, and only secondarily is treatment appraised on the basis of the world of experience—to the neuroses as seen in the private practice group under consideration, the situation is reversed. Here the *primary* referent in appraising the results of treatment resides in the patient's *experience* in living and, while behavioral patterns are not irrelevant, they are not the primary point of reference. In fact, it may be quite plausible for the patient to seek treatment and to receive it even though his behavior, in the social sense at least, may be exemplary. This will be discussed further.

The emergence of a psychotic state, marked as it invariably is by gross behavioral signs, inevitably makes for a shift in therapeutic approach and in the modes of appraising treatment. In this connection, the psychiatrist has long been faced with a tantalizing unanswered and perhaps unanswerable question. It is a common impression that a not insignificant number of persons seek outpatient care who do not give any blatantly evident signs of behavioral disturbance, but who are faced with imminent psychotic disorganization, including the disintegration of social behavior. The treatment process in such instances may avert the behavioral display, but, unfortunately, we cannot think of a way of conclusively demonstrating that a psychosis was averted that never occurred!

At first glance, it might seem far-fetched to draw parallels based on the difference between the neuroses and the psychoses and as apparently disparate a matter as the difference between two groups of neurotic patients of markedly different socioeconomic origins. By means of contrasting the patients in a short-term therapy research project and the patients in private practice, it can be demonstrated that, even in different outpatient situations with neurotic patients, variable levels of emphasis on behavioral as opposed to experiential modalities come into play. This emphasis influences the type of therapy used and the appraisal of therapeutic results.

The neurotic patients of lower socioeconomic groups, which make up a part of this study, are those in a short-term therapy research project under the direction of Dr. Eugene Meyer at the

Hopkins.[5] These patients are substantially all from the lowest socioeconomic group, this being the nature of the referrals obtained. Their presenting social and economic situations were of long standing, usually from birth, including limited cultural and educational opportunities. This contributed to a mental set and body of expectations on their part in connection with the psychiatrist different from those of the private patients of much higher socioeconomic background. In the project, a fixed limit of ten weekly interviews was announced to the patient in advance. Tangentially, one of the particular questions that prompted the institution of this project was whether a modicum of treatment could be offered to a group who notoriously do not start treatment or, if they do, drop out after one or two visits.

The short-term treatment research project includes an attempt to establish certain quantifiable data to be obtained from the patient, in addition to the usual statistical information and the evaluations of the therapist. The intent is as objective a measure as possible of the results of therapy. The instruments employed include a symptom check list of 50 items: 17 have to do with physical symptoms, 20 with intrapersonal experience (phobias, compulsive activities, feelings of guilt), and 13 with interpersonal experiences (paranoidal or being critical of others, feeling dependent on others). Another check list attempts to appraise the level of mood and energy of the patient, as well as the sort of data, much less manageable for research purposes, deriving from personal interviews with the patient.

Even in this admittedly crude instrument for evaluating the state and progression of the patient in the briefest of treatment processes, and with this socioculturally deprived group, heavy emphasis is placed on the inner experiences and mood of the patient. Behavior and social behavior are relevant, but the assumption is made that they derive from inner experience and not the reverse. The socioeconomic impact within the short-term treatment project group, however, brought certain issues into much bolder relief than they might be in other brief-treatment situations where this is not so significant a factor.

It is a very difficult matter to spell out just what the differences are between the therapeutic approach to the project patients and to private psychotherapeutic and psychoanalytic patients other than the factor of time. The contradictions between the behavioral and the experiential aspects of the treatment process seem to throw some light on the problem. By this, it is not inferred that the short-term treatment is simply directive and that new patterns of behavior are suggested as such, or that attention is directed primarily to the relief of symptoms. Its goals are more immediately oriented, however, towards experiments in living that may modify entrenched repetitive kinds of attitudes and behavior. It is tempting to assume that, since the treatment period is so short and the group a deprived one, considerations of dynamics, unconscious conflict, and transference phenomena can be excluded, and that on this basis a sharp line of division can be established between it and psychoanalysis. None of these criteria are true in any absolute sense of the term, however, and although they are likely true in the quantitative sense, truth is not easy to demonstrate. In general the short-term treatment process is oriented towards the reinforcement of previously employed comparatively healthy modes of character defense. Clarifications and interpretations, when made, are apt to be in the sphere of bringing into consciousness previously concealed emotions—for instance: "Your headache seemed to arise after that incident with your mother; can you recall how you were feeling at the time?" Here again, we are faced with a kind of approach by no means alien in itself to the psychoanalytic except for the elusive factor of quantity, and the same might be said for transference and genetic data, and so on.

On the basis of a superficial examination, one is prone to be overimpressed by the exogenous or situational factors in seeking explanations for their emotional disturbances. In the psychiatric role, however, it is more useful to assume that their neurotic problems derive from endogenous factors, at least at this time of their lives. This is so despite the fact that life-long severe socioeconomic deprivation undoubtedly does influence family stability and the possibilities for individual emotional growth—a theme elaborated on later. It should be stressed that this bias depends on the role of the psychiatrist and the particular skills that he can bring to bear. This is not to say that insofar as socioeconomic factors are relevant sources of distress for such patients they might not be dealt with by other persons of appropriate skills in those areas.

The role of the psychiatrist is being threatened from yet another source, the present cultural situation. Emphasis on the need for psychiatric services for the underprivileged has invited a diffusion of the identity of the psychiatrist. The valid connection of emotional disability with disadvantaged social circumstances has been taken by many to mean that the psychiatrist should be the central figure in any attack on social ills to the inevitable sacrifice of his specific role as psychiatrist. This view tends to depreciate the skills and contributions of the social worker, the social engineer, and the slum-clearance experts, and in any properly conceived attack on human unhappiness, all of these skills must be used. Insofar as we are considering the special skills of the psychiatrist, it would seem that it is just here that he is capable of making unique contributions, and that there is no particular reason why his skills would especially qualify him to be the primary force in broad social programs.

Lifelong sociocultural and educational deprivation limits, perhaps irrevocably, the capacity for certain modes of experiences. Nevertheless, the widespread pessimism [9] is unwarranted that such persons are not fit subjects for psychotherapy, and already one may believe that the present research project will give evidence to support this opinion. Of course, in conducting psychotherapy with the lower socioeconomic group, one must be cognizant of the particular skewing and stunting of character development and function within the limitations imposed by them.

Some interesting parallels can be drawn between the psychotic and the socioeconomically deprived groups that bear on the goals of treatment. While the two groups are certainly grossly different in character, they have the common characteristic of having limitations in the capacity for certain modes of experience and varieties of aesthetic as well as cognitive appreciation. This includes limitations in the ability to create and elaborate constructive abstractions of thought and to integrate the emotions as a substantially constructive force in their life experience. This is true in the psychotic group primarily because of massively deprived family situations and in the lower socioeconomic group because of a massively deprived social situation with its inevitable secondary impingement on the family.

The same theses have been discussed more extensively by the author,[6] and Brody [2] has employed them in a consideration of "borderline states." Chronic long-continued low-grade traumata are more apt to be primary etiologic factors in the emotional disorders than acute crises, and the psychotic and the lower socioeconomic groups have had a far greater exposure to such factors than the higher socioeconomic neurotic or the normal groups. It has been demonstrated [4] that mental disorders can be reduced in a lower socioeconomic community by offering better economic and educational opportunities and increasing the opportunities for social functioning.

Having arrived at an impasse; and being unable to write off short-term treatment even with the project patients as simply "supportive therapy," the psychoanalytic patients were evaluated in order to see whether anything could be discovered that would aid in the differentiation. Here all the processes mentioned above are employed but more extensively, and particularly so in the exploration of the developmental and transference aspects of present modes of experiencing and behaving. The psychoanalytic patient's motivations and goals in treatment play a critical role in differentiating the two situations and hence in appraising the results of treatment.

Better social and economic opportunities, including educational, make for a higher level of motivation and capacity to engage in treatment. Although some feel that the greater ability of this group to engage in treatment is derived from the greater concurrence between the social group of patient and therapist, this is not the crucial factor. The psychoanalytic patients are more verbal, more introspective, and more prone to seek changes in their experiential modalities. They come for help seeking not only relief from inner pain, relief of a symptom, or help in the modification of a pressing environmental situation. These symptoms are often the presenting complaints, the ticket of admission. This, more often than not, derives from the erroneous assumption, based in prior experience with others and transferred to the psychoanalyst, that only by means of such symptoms would they elicit his sympathy and help.[1] They often suffer from feelings, poorly formulated verbally, that their experience in living is narrowed and restricted by conflictual and chaotic feelings and that they wish help in modifying it.

It is not suggested that the psychoanalytic patients are lacking in neurotic motivations or are not seeking neurotic goals that would be modified or given up altogether in the successful treatment. In addition, however, there is a legitimate request that transcends simple relief from symptoms and pain, and reaches out for a new mode of existence. Whatever the level of their social performance may be, and it is often very good indeed, they feel that life as an existential experience lacks fullness and direction. They seek a drastically new mode of being; and treatment, to the degree that it is successful, is a creative experience.

When one turns from the project group to the psychoanalytic group, the psychoanalyst's experience is also different in quality. In the project group, it is more behaviorial or mechanistic; in the psychoanalytic, more experiential. In it, he functions much more in the realm of an empathic living in and with the patient, while hopefully retaining his own perspective and evaluative potential. It might be said that this is not universally true—and it is certainly far from true with many psychotic persons, where indeed the degree of experiential involvement on the part of the therapist is intense—but the distinction is accurate. If one thinks of effectual therapeutic intervention, rather than simply involvement in the general sense, then the principle certainly holds, since our therapeutic results with psychotics have been at best limited. It may be that the treating person recoils from the very intensity of experiential involvement with both psychotic and culturally deprived, but by and large constructive experiential involvement tends not to occur.

Differing character structures and motivations, deriving from differing individuals and social situations, determine the attitudes towards treatment of the various classes of patients under consideration. The capacity for primarily behavioral or primarily experiential change on the patient's part is a basic factor in the choice of treatment and on the resultant technique and attitude of the treating person.

As true in experimental psychology as well as in psychiatry and psychoanalysis, the problem of any sort of objective appraisal of the present state of affairs or of the projected course of events becomes enormously more complex when one shifts from the strictly behavioral frame of reference to that of private experience, the world of ideas and feelings. Skinner [8] has suggested that the study of behavior alone is the only relevant frame of reference for the study of man, without recourse to introspection. Much can be said for this as an experimental hypothesis, but in the healing professions and elsewhere, it would seem that the world of human experience and the subtlety of human emotion can hardly be excluded for a purely mechanistic view. The increasing sophistication of the experimentalist and his ability to ask searching questions based on behaviorial patterns, including verbal behavior, is impressive. Undoubtedly, major contributions to understanding in psychiatry will be forthcoming from this group. However, the necessary fragmentation intrinsic to scientific methodology emphasizes rather than denies the need for the holistic approach as represented by psychiatry and psychoanalysis, with whatever sacrifice this may include for the scientific method.

One should stress that the thesis developed here does not negate a behavioral psychology but does define its limitations. There are undoubtedly important correlations between inner experience and behavior and adequate social performance. The field of introspective psychology and of interpersonal psychiatry and psychoanalysis would be crippled without reference to the subtleties of behavior, including, for that matter, verbal behavior. Man, however, is not simply what he does but is also, and more particularly, what he thinks and feels as well, and these latter spheres are a fit subject for treatment when they are the source of discomfort and pain. To suffer from inhibition in aesthetic experience deserves no less therapeutic attention than the suffering deriving from inhibition in the more mundane activities of living.

Particularly now, when psychotherapy of one sort or another is being more widely employed, does the question of the appraisal of goals in treatment and the techniques of measuring the results of treatment deserve scrutiny. The results of therapy cannot be appraised simply on the basis of such common denominators as they may have. To illustrate, if the combination of inner lack of conflict and social conformity were chosen as the basis on which we were to appraise the results of all therapies, then George Orwell [7] would have described the ideal state of affairs in *1984*. This is not to say that these goals are intrinsically poor, or that in the more profoundly ill of our patients we would not more than willingly welcome their attainment. The span of psychiatric treatment is broader than this, however, and the problem is far more complicated.

The level of inner comfort alone as a measure of freedom from emotional disorder is deceptive. It has even been suggested [8] that mental health might be defined as a state of dynamic equilibrium between id, ego, and superego and without reference directly to social factors at all. If one turns to the creative person, however, it would seem that his creativity resides in the very state of disequilibrium that would presumably deny him mental health. Yet neurosis and creativity cannot simply be equated. Moral and ethical—that is, social—factors play a constructive role in creativity as they do not in neurosis. Thus mental states can only be defined when proper cognizance is also given to the constant impingement of the environment upon the individual. If living is to be a positive experience, it must inevitably include the pain of stresses and conflicts within the self and from time to time with the sociocultural situation as well.

Crucial to the dilemma of comparing the results of treatment, even were one to assume a common goal for all treatment programs, is the impossibility of ever again reproducing the precise state of affairs that existed when treatment was begun. This denies the direct possibility of the comparison of one treatment method with another in the same patient, or of comparing treatment with no treatment. Now, for research purposes, there is the clear possibility of comparing numbers of patients, using statistical techniques. Some of the admittedly crude devices of this sort, which are used in the project, have been described earlier in this chapter. In attempting to work out the appropriate treatment program for a given patient in a two-person situation, however, such devices are of little comfort.

Conclusion

It has been demonstrated by means of the two examples, comparing psychotic with neurotic patients, and socioeconomically lower and upper class neurotic patients, that the motivations of the patient deriving from his character structure play a major role in the determination of the treatment plan and in the appraisal of its success or failure. This has long been a source of concern, since the psychiatrist and psychoanalyst, coming into their disciplines from medicine, have tended to place undue emphasis on the physician as the sole dictator of the treatment plan. Not only can this precept be questioned in psychiatry but in medicine as well. Insofar as treatment results are concerned, their appraisal can be made only in terms of the aims of treatment, and no all-encompassing yardstick can be created to measure different aims. It is self-evident that behavioral goals, to the degree that they constitute relatively more manifest goals in the psychotic and project patients, will be more readily measurable than in other neurotic, and particularly psychoanalytic, patients, where the results are primarily in the sphere of inner experience.

REFERENCES

1. Balint, M.: The Doctor, His Patient and the Illness, New York, Internat Univ Press, 1957.

2. Brody, E. B.: Borderline state, character disorder, and psychotic manifestations—some conceptual formulations, Psychiatry 23:75-80, 1960.

3. Lampl deGroot, J.: Symptom formation and character formation, Int J Psychoanal 44:1-11, 1963.

4. Leighton, A. H.: Poverty and social change, Sci Amer 212:21-27, 1965.

5. Meyer, E., et al.: Limited psychotherapy in an outpatient psychosomatic clinic, read at the annual meeting of the Amer Psychiat Assn, May, 1966.

6. Novey, S.: The principle of working through in psychoanalysis, J Amer Psychoanal Ass 10:658-676, 1962.

7. Orwell, G.: "1984," New York, Harcourt, 1949.

8. Skinner, B. F.: Evolution and man's progress, Daedalus 90:534, 1961.

9. Yamamoto, J., and Goin, M. K.: On the treatment of the poor, Amer J Psychiat 122:267-273, 1965.

Discussion

ROBERT A. COHEN, MD

*Director, Clinical Investigations, National Institute of
Mental Health, Bethesda*

DR. NOVEY HAS DISCUSSED at least four important issues, each of
them worthy of this entire two-day meeting. First, patients come
to psychotherapy with significantly different goals. Some are concerned primarily with troubled behavior in which they are engaged willy-nilly; others show few or no behavioral disturbances,
but are rather involved in the dilemma that Paul Tillich has described as that of men who stand on boundaries: "They experience unrest, insecurity, and limitations of existence in many
forms. They know the impossibility of attaining serenity, security,
and perfection."

Second, psychotic patients of all social classes and working-class
neurotic patients tend to fall in a group that seeks primarily behavioral change; the typical middle-class person who seeks psychoanalysis often is more concerned with coming to terms with his
inner unrest and insecurity. These differences in goals naturally
affect the type of treatment prescribed and thus determine the
results achieved.

Third, most studies of therapeutic outcome take little cognizance of these differences in goals and in the therapeutic techniques employed and therefore, in a sense, compare apples and
oranges. Evaluation efforts are further complicated by the fact that
assessment of progress toward behavioral goals is more susceptible
to objective measurements than alterations in inner experience or
structural changes in personality.

Fourth, some of the limitations in personality attributes qualitatively similar in both groups may result from early and chronic
deprivation-experiences and/or other varieties of low-level
traumata.

163

I found myself resonating to each of these themes, recalling experiences that confirmed or slightly modified Dr. Novey's contentions. But I have decided to stray from the purely clinical setting to mention a few studies from other fields that bear on the differences between the working- and middle-class individuals to whom he referred.

A study [1] on the management and instruction of normal and mentally retarded children found that normal middle-class children perform best with the intangible reward of teacher's spoken approval. In contrast, normal children from working-class families and mentally retarded children from all social classes do best when offered tangible rewards, such as tokens or prizes.

Over ten years ago, scholars [2] became intrigued by the rather primitive concept of the schizophrenogenic mother in vogue then. They studied a carefully assembled cohort of individuals who had been hospitalized with a diagnosis of schizophrenia, and compared them and their families with a matched group of classmates who had not developed any emotional disorder. They found that the higher status controls reported mothers as having relatively weak authority roles, while the schizophrenic patients with whom they were paired more often reported maternal dominance. At lower status levels, this difference between control and schizophrenic families washed out; mothers were described as dominant in both the normal control and index families. This led the researchers to a series of studies concerning social class and parent-child relationship.[3] They took as their point of departure the proposition that members of different social classes, by virtue of enjoying or suffering different conditions of life, come to see the world differently— to develop different conceptions of social reality and of the desirable, and different aspirations, hopes and fears. These values become the bridge between position in the social structure and the behavior of the individual. Despite wide variations within each social class, and despite the fact that they hold many values in common, the evidence was clear that the line that separates manual from nonmanual workers has profound consequences for both values and behavior.

Middle-class occupations characteristically deal more with the manipulation of ideas, symbols, and interpersonal relations; working-class jobs more with the manipulation of things. Middle-class occupations are more subject to self-direction; working-class jobs more to standardization and direct supervision. Getting ahead in the middle class is more dependent on one's own actions; in the working class, one depends more on collective action—especially where the industry is unionized. The behavior conceived of as desirable for one's self and one's children varies with these different conditions of life. In general, working-class individuals value obedience, neatness, and cleanliness more highly than the middle class; the middle-class persons place a higher value on curiosity, consideration for others, happiness, and self-control. The working-class parents center on conformity to external proscription; the middle-class on self-direction. To the working class, it is the overt act that matters; in the middle class, motives and feelings are of greater concern. In general, the working class takes a traditional, the middle class a developmental, point of view.

Admittedly, such is an oversimplified view of a complex issue, but nevertheless it is safe to say that the working-class individual looks for something outside himself, something concrete and immediate; his middle-class counterpart, in contrast, searches within himself for motives and meanings. These are pervasive values, reciprocally related to the conditions of life of the two classes, and it seems to me that they are consistent with the clinical observations to which Dr. Novey has called our attention. It is worth mentioning that these findings have been confirmed in other cultures, and that the research group is now undertaking a more specific study of the relationship between occupations and values in an attempt to find out how the requirements and experiences in a variety of jobs and professions join with other processes to influence personality and behavior.

Having established that a significant difference exists between middle- and working-class values and, with somewhat less validity, the possibility that parents of middle-class schizophrenic patients share more values with working-class parents than the parents of middle-class normals, we seem to have come up with a rather neat hypothesis about the possible influences of experiential factors in the development and/or maintenance of schizophrenic behavior. The excess incidence reported of schizophrenia in the working class offers some support for the proposition that individuals raised with these particular values, and subjected also to the manifold stresses of life in this culture, are more susceptible to a schizophrenic illness than we more fortunate middle-class individuals. This view may have some truth, but it is far from proved. Too many findings conflict and too little evidence is solid. Perhaps I should also call attention to the fact that much of what Dr. Novey said applied to differences between the middle class and the working class—but that the poverty-stricken, whom he includes in his observations, were excluded from the research studies that I have mentioned.

Although findings conflict, in all probability more schizophrenia is produced at lower socioeconomic levels. The question is: Why? I am fairly sure that we do not actually disagree, but I would be even more positive than Dr. Novey was in attributing it to factors other than the stunting of personality growth by the excessive stresses and strains of lower-class existence. I doubt that the differences we have described between the middle and working class really reflect different levels in maturity of the personality, the middle class's affinity for psychoanalysis notwithstanding. A developmental hypothesis seems to me at least equally powerful; this would lead us to conclude that the different goals and responses in psychotherapy reflect differences in personalities that are finely attuned to demands of their different and expectable life-situations.

If we turn our attention away from the similarities in values between middle-class parents of schizophrenic patients and all working-class parents, then we find that there is one striking finding that distinguishes families who number a schizophrenic individual among them from all other families, regardless of social class. I refer to the work of Dr. Lyman Wynne and his associates.

They [4,5] found that much of the earlier difficulty in distinguishing between communication of both middle- and lower-class families, with and without schizophrenic members, was due to the fact that attention had been focused on the content of speech and thought—particularly true of the poorly educated group. Content does vary markedly with social class, education, and culture; and the speech and concerns of families whose members had at most a grade-school education could not, in many instances, easily be compared to that of middle-class families. But others [6] found—when attention was directed to ways in which parents of lower-class schizophrenic individuals linked ideas together, how they organized their thoughts, and how well they succeeded in achieving closure—that they displayed the same difficulty in establishing shared foci of attention and in communication of consensually understood meanings as the parents of middle-class schizophrenic individuals. Further, these patterns of impairment were not found in normals of any social class. Cross-cultural studies in Japan and

Lebanon, including some studies of families who were totally illiterate, supported these findings. As expected, these observations have raised a wholly new set of questions. The evidence strongly suggests that the similarity in treatment goals of all schizophrenic and lower-class nonschizophrenic patients, which Dr. Novey has described, do not have the same psychodynamic origin. Work on the nature of the inner experiences of the middle-class schizophrenic patient has been carried out for many years at this hospital and at Chestnut Lodge. But psychoanalysts have spent too little time with working-class patients of the type described by Dr. Novey—primarily because they were not suitable for treatment by classical technique. It is most gratifying, therefore, to hear about the study in which Drs. Meyer and Novey are engaged, and about the exciting project Dr. Wagner described yesterday. I believe that observations from their work will lead to important extensions in personality theory; they will help also in bringing to a group of patients ordinarily subjected to treatment much too limited to physiological and biochemical interventions some consideration and engagement of their thinking and feeling.

REFERENCES

1. Zigler, E. T.: Rigidity in performance of the feeble-minded, NIMH Res Grant #3945, Yale University, unpublished report.

2. Kohn, M. L., and Clausen, J. A.: Parental authority behavior and schizophrenia, Amer J Orthopsychiat *26*:297-316, 1956.

3. a. Kohn, M. L.: Social class and parental values, Amer J Sociol *64*:337-351, 1959.

b. ——: Social class and the exercise of parental authority, Amer Sociol Rev *24*:326-352, 1959.

c. Kohn, M. L., and Carroll, E. E.: Social class and the allocation of parental responsibilities, Sociometry *23*:372-392, 1960.

d. Kohn, M. L.: Social class and parent-child relationships: an interpretation, Amer J Sociol *68*:471-480, 1963.

4. Wynne, L. C., and Singer, M. T.: Thought disorder and family relations of schizophrenics, I. A research strategy; II. Classification of forms of thinking, Arch Gen Psychiat (Chicago) *9*:191-206, 1963; III. Methodology using projective techniques; IV. Results and implications, Arch Gen Psychiat (Chicago) *12*:187-212, 1965.

5. Wynne, L. C., and Singer, M. T.: Communication styles in parents of normals, neurotics, and schizophrenics, Psychiat Res Rep Amer Psychiat Ass *20*:25-38, 1966.

6. Wild, C., et al.: Measuring disordered styles of thinking. Using the object sorting test on parents of schizophrenic patients, Arch Gen Psychiat (Chicago) *13*:471-476, 1965.

8

On the Concept of Health

Francis McLaughlin, MD

Private Practice of Psychoanalysis, Baltimore, Director,
The Baltimore Psychoanalytic Institute, 1953-1959

The concept of health must be approached affirmatively. Not merely the absence of illness, mental health implies a certain constancy, with flexibility and openness to new ideas and experiences. Even adaptation and relation to reality, however important, hold only for particular situations. A person cannot be deemed healthy at all times and under all circumstances.

THE DEVELOPMENT OF PSYCHOANALYTIC THEORY and technique began in illness and pathology. Instinct and defense against instinct were the first objects of Freud's interest. The conflicts that arose as a result of these processes became the subject of intensive study, and attempts to understand the various factors that led to neurosis became the predominant interest of the early analysts. This was a natural development; it is evident that it was a logical approach to any understanding of mental processes.

However, in the gradual evolution of the effort to develop a general theory of psychic functioning, more emphasis and attention were devoted to the usual course of maturation; less emphasis was placed on pathology and more on the ordinary course of human development. This process got its first emphasis from Freud's *The Ego and the Id*,[2] his later *Inhibitions, Symptoms and Anxiety*,[3] Anna Freud's *The Ego and the Mechanism of Defense*,[1] Hartmann's various papers and particularly his monograph, *Ego Psychology and the Problem of Adaptation*.[5]

Many factors direct our attention to a consideration of the concept of health. One's attitude towards what is healthy and what is sick exerts an influence on therapeutic and technical thought. These ideas influence our recommendations whether treatment is or is not indicated, what kind of therapy we see as necessary, what changes we deem advisable, and what criteria we use for termination of any therapeutic situation. Differences in outlook on this point influence our choice of patients, our criteria of what is treatable, and, in large part, our technical approach. Moreover, this is a topic worthy of consideration in its own right, to see what general principles can be derived. This last position will be the point of view of this chapter. The author has stated [8]:

> Such a point of view indicates strongly the need for careful evaluation of the entire range of personality types if psychoanalysis is truly to become a general theory of psychology. . . . it delineates for us the urgency of well-constructed studies of the exceptions, why some persons are more open to the unexpected and why some . . . are more able to provide new solutions. . . . a need for more . . . attempts to understand competence, success and genius, and the average member of the community. . . . Too much emphasis is placed on pathology and not enough on health. . . . This recommends the . . . study of the available range of possibilities open to us.

As we consider this problem, we become aware of its complexity. Wallerstein outlined one basic issue: "what theoretically constitutes the ideal state of mental health and the unavoidable impingements upon efforts at its empirical assessment by value judgments as well as by the vantage point and the partisan interests of the judge."[10]

Two seemingly opposite points of view exist. Lampl-DeGroot[7] excluded cultural factors, since she felt that estimates of sickness and health should be independent of these variables.

> From a scientific point of view, we have, I think, to follow a different line. We speak of bodily health when the various organs of the body function in such a way that stimuli from inside as well as from outside can be assimilated and vital processes are not disturbed. In psychology . . . we should consider a person to be in psychic health when the different areas of the mind have reached a cooperation leading to optimum mental functioning. . . . We have to look upon the nature of the ego organization, and especially at the disposition to its synthesizing capacity, in order to decide between mental health and sickness.

Judgments in social terms are moral or value judgments and excluded from scientific consideration.

Ruesch[9] takes what is apparently an opposing view: "Mental health is obviously defined in terms of the culture in which the patient and the therapist live."

These two points of view, rather than being irreconcilable, stress two aspects of the problem, each leaving out the other. The ego, in Lampl-DeGroot's formulation, is not only derived from internal pressures but also is a composite of attitudes arising from identifications with other persons (primarily parents) as well as cultural norms. Ruesch emphasizes the cultural and neglects the introjective; the process that leads to internalization and intrapsychic conflict is not given proper weight. In combining the two points of view, we get a broader perspective.

Certain things seem to become clear as we think about this problem. Primarily, health cannot be considered a statistical norm. Subjective valuations play an important role. Cultural, social and personal values enter the mix, as we see in the examples above. Health sometimes is seen as equivalent to "perfection." It is sometimes defined as freedom from symptoms—clearly too simple a definition. Aside from the difficulty of saying what is a symptom and what an achievement, this view completely avoids the problem of the character neuroses, which, in many instances, are "symptom" free.

Our view of health plays a large role in our relation with our fellowmen. We may hide feelings of inferiority or superiority by relating to others as sick. Freud pointed out quite early, for instance, that analysts may protect themselves against their own neuroses by their insistence on analyzing others. This may be an important determinant in the choice of psychiatry as a profession.

Let us now go to more specific considerations of this problem. In any individual, the strength of his drives and his ego-organization are independent variables. There has been a tendency to view conflict and mechanisms of defense as pathologic in themselves. It is important to stress that these concepts carry no such implication. As Hartmann [5] clearly delineates, adaptation and achievements in dealing with the self and the world must assume increasing importance in our thinking. Conflict and failures in adaptation can be a regular and useful part of development. The same is true in treatment, where pathologic reactions, such as regression and transference distortions, can be utilized in the search for health.

The concept of health varies. Some of its variables reflect the aims that one sets for oneself, his basic views on human growth, and his cultural views. There is always the risk of allowing our ideas to become determined by moral and other subjective goals.

Freud understood that there was a dualistic problem: to understand the instinctual life of the individual, to be equally aware of his rational behavior. A common mistake has been to equate id and biologic, ego and nonbiologic. Hartmann [5] had clearly demonstrated the common biologic origins of these structures. At various times in our history, the tendency has been to glorify the instinctual man or conversely to exalt the man of reason, as if this were an either/or proposition.

Between reason and successful adaptation, there is a connection. "We should not take it for granted, however, that the recognition of reality is the equivalent of adaptation of reality." [6] The most rational attitudes do not necessarily constitute an optimum for purposes of adaptation. Rationality may be, for instance, a defense against appropriate affect or action.

Hartmann [6] has made clear that a "correct" view of reality is not the sole criterion of whether an action is in accordance with reality. A healthy person should be able to employ a system of rational control, but also to recognize and make allowances for the irrational nature of other mental activities. The rational man must be able to incorporate the irrational and have tolerance for it—and, I might add, profit from it. The automatic and rigid rejection of the irrational is in itself a form of illness.

Mobility and plasticity of the ego is a prerequisite for health. However, a healthy ego is not always plastic; sometimes we must say: so far and no further. We have only to remember that at times even the most healthy person must allow some of his ego functions to be temporarily suspended, as in orgasm or in dreams. A tolerance of "id" control, rather than a terror of it, is essential at times.

Health is not to be equated with freedom from anxiety, guilt or shame. In the healthy person, there may be occasions when such feelings are fitting. Their appropriateness is what distinguishes them from their neurotic equivalents. In the healthy person, there must also be a tolerance (not an excuse) for less than maximum performance at all times.

Conflict is part and parcel of man's development. It provides a necessary stimulus for structure formation. There is no correlation between healthy and pathologic behavior so far as its origin in defense is concerned.

Lampl-DeGroot [7] stressed that the outcome of not only external but intrasystemic conflict depends on the relative intactness of the ego. Its synthetic and integrative capacities must be adequate to the task. The ego (and the superego) must allow sufficient satisfaction of instinctual and affective needs, but provide also consideration for the external world. In essence, the ego must reconcile all these demands without compromising its integrity. It must encompass both the pleasure principle and the reality principle. It is important to stress that conflict is never eliminated, either in an old problem or in a new. Even in the most healthy person, infantile strivings may remain active and appear in consciousness with relative frequency. The essential differences lie in that they are recognized as infantile, that they do not determine behavior or attitude, and that they can be repudiated, not dealt with by archaic and unconscious defenses.

Dynamic and economic factors always operate. A successful defense, for instance, may be a failure in relation to adaptation. We have only to consider the defense of isolation or undoing or repression, which contains the conflict but cripples the person in his living. Conversely, failure of one of these defenses may provide a positive stimulus for investigation and growth.

Kris's concept of "regression in the service of the ego" is familiar and useful, and has shown us that the shortest way to reality is not always the best. This withdrawal often leads to increased mastery of thinking and creativity. In contrast, we often think of turning away as pathologic. Every day, we see this process in operation in the transference neurosis.

We must return to the idea that rational thought and activity, the synthetic and differentiating functions of the ego, are not sufficient for optimum adaptation. This organized system is essential, but it needs also a tolerance to allow and encompass more primitive systems.

Too often defense, the various stages of development, and modes of reaction tend to be related to illness. Well-being is seen as a state in which these ubiquitous factors are considered absent. There may be reluctance to recognize how strong a role they play in the healthy person. Conversely, when we undertake the analysis of the "normal" patient, we become aware how crippling can be some of the conduct and attitudes seemingly directed toward reality.

When we consider the concept of health, it is useful to approach it from an affirmative point of view. What are this person's relations with an adaptation to reality? Since reality can vary, our ideas about health must be flexible. Perhaps health can be defined in a general way as a sense of self-preservation and self-expression.

As Hartmann [5] pointed out, it is important to understand that adaptation is definable only in relation to specific environmental settings. It can never be considered in the abstract. Furthermore, the actual state of equilibrium of an individual tells us little or nothing about his capacity for adaptation. We must investigate and evaluate his relations with the external world. Capacity for achievement and enjoyment considered in isolation tell us little. The indispensable factor in estimating a person's powers of adaptation is evaluating his relationship with the "typical average environment." The processes of adaptation are always appropriate to a limited range of environmental conditions.

It is an interesting point that disturbances in achieving and enjoying cannot simply be evaluated as signs of failure in adaptation. Successful attempts at adaptation in relation to specific situations may lead at the same time to general restrictions in adaptation affecting the individual. We have only to think of certain mechanisms of defense that lead to successful adjustment in the external world yet adversely affect the individual.

All this brings out an important concept: that the process of defense always serves a dual purpose—that is, mastery over instincts, and accommodation with the external world. Depending on the makeup of the individual and the environment to which the individual must adapt, the balance between these two functions may be crucial. Looking at it this way makes clear that successful accommodation with the external world may sometimes be purchased at a price. The dilemma brings into focus how carefully we must consider our attitudes toward this question. Hopefully, the "healthy" man may have a choice in this decision.

Closely tied to this question of adaptation is the ability to synthesize. As Hartmann [6] again makes clear, synthesis is a prerequisite for adaptation but also dependent on the degree of adaptation attained. With adaptation and synthesis as basic considerations, we begin to see the development of an "evolutionary concept" of health.[6] These capacities, dependent on each other, are primarily dependent on ego-id balances, both constitutional and developmental. Thus, to a certain extent, they are influenced by inherited factors.

In many ways, this brings to the fore quantitative considerations. Structural ones are important, but the ability to erect stable structures to a considerable extent may be influenced by quantitative factors, again both constitutional and developmental. We have only to consider that mechanisms that lead to psychopathology can, under different circumstances, serve adaptive purposes. The more possible it is for functions to become autonomous and move into the "conflict free" area, the greater is the possibility of a healthy adaptation.

In summary, we may say that mental health is a positive quality, not merely the absence of illness. Health implies a certain constancy; however, life is not a static process. Learning, we hope, continues throughout life. Therefore, in addition to constancy, there needs to be flexibility and an openness to new ideas and experiences. It is perhaps superfluous to observe that health is not necessarily synonymous with "happiness." Freud spoke of the "everyday unhappiness" against which the healthy person must defend himself, and with which he must come to terms.

Health is always a relative term. We have spoken of its relationship to environment. All we can say is that we deem a person healthy in the here and now—not that he will be at all times and under all circumstances. Freud makes the point cogently in his discussion of the limitations of the psychoanalytic approach.[4] Any adaptation holds good for only the particular situation and time.

Perhaps this chapter has raised a question or two. However, if it has pointed out some of the ambiguities, complexities and contradictions inherent in this problem, and indicated areas for further study, maybe it has performed a useful function.

REFERENCES

1. Freud, A.: The Ego and the Mechanisms of Defense, New York, Internat Univ Press, 1946.
2. Freud, S.: The Ego and the Id, London, Standard Edition, 1923.
3. ———: Inhibitions, Symptoms and Anxiety, London, Standard Edition, 1926.
4. ———: Analysis terminable and interminable, Collected Papers, vol. V, London, Hogarth Press, 1937.
5. Hartmann, H.: Ego Psychology and the Problem of Adaptation, New York, Internat Univ Press, 1938.

6. ————: The Concept of Health; Essays on Ego Psychology, New York, Internat Univ Press, 1964.

7. Lampl-deGroot, J.: Symptom formation and character formation, Int J Psychoanal *44*:1-11, 1963.

8. McLaughlin, F.: Some considerations for the further development of psychoanalysis, Int J Psychoanal *44*:454-460, 1963.

9. Ruesch, J.: Communication, the Social Matrix of Society, New York, Norton, 1951.

10. Wallerstein, R. S.: The goals of psychoanalysis: a survey of analytic viewpoints, J Amer Psychoanal Ass *13*:748-770, 1965.

Discussion

MARVIN L. ADLAND, MD

Private Practice of Psychoanalysis, Washington

SHEPPARD-PRATT SPARKLES at this time of its life because it has shown that very remarkable capacity for constancy and constructive adaptation that Dr. McLaughlin views as ingredients of mental health. The Hospital was founded on a value system that was and is tolerant, while offering opportunity to each person for change and maturation. In the turbulent years of World War II, when all value systems were in flux and crisis, it provided for me, in a very personal way, both a constancy, by virtue of what it stood for, and an opportunity for growth, by virtue of contact with my new teachers and friends, including Dr. McLaughlin.

Dr. McLaughlin wonders why some people are open to the unexpected, why some are more able to provide new solutions, what is healthy and what is sick, and what are some basic general principles applicable to the concept of mental health. There are extremes in the definition of mental health from the complete inclusion to the complete exclusion of cultural factors and social and moral value systems. As he has worked between these extremes, Dr. McLaughlin has written:

> The ego, in Lampl-DeGroot's formulation, is not only derived from internal pressures but also is composite of attitudes arising from identifications with other persons (primarily parents) as well as cultural norms. . . . In any individual, the strength of his drives and his ego-organization are independent variables. . . . Health is not to be equated with freedom from anxiety, guilt or shame. In the healthy person, there may be occasions when such feelings are fitting. Their appropriateness is what distinguishes them from their neurotic equivalents. . . . Conflict is part and parcel of man's development. It provides a necessary stimulus for structure formation. . . . All this brings out an important con-

176

cept: that the process of defense always serves a dural purpose—
that is, mastery over instincts, and accommodation with the external world . . . the balance between these two functions may be
crucial. . . . In summary, we may say that mental health is a
positive quality, not merely the absence of illness. Health implies
a certain constancy . . . flexibility and an openness to new ideas
and experiences.

It appears to me that our psychoanalytic investigations have
made great strides in understanding and treating our inner psychic processes. But if the definition of health includes, as I think it
must, the capacity for "openness to new ideas and experiences,"
we must not be content to understand and modify our capacity for
adaptation, we must also be concerned about the reality and value
systems to which we are responding, the experiences, the cultural
norms that help form our ego. While inside our offices we may be
focusing on the mechanism of defense, outside our offices we are
equally obligated actively to participate in modifying the reality.
And, in the office, what about the reality? I believe that the influence of the culture and the value systems has broad implications
for the world we live in, for our communities, hospitals and, ultimately, each individual.

The Center for the Study of Democratic Institutions recently
printed a speech by Senator Fulbright [1] in which he considered the
political implications of this same issue. He said: "it is interesting
that the war that began in 1861 was referred to in Massachusetts as
the 'rebellion of the Southern States,' in Pennsylvania as the 'Civil
War,' in Virginia as the 'War between the States,' and in Texas as
the 'war to repel Yankee aggression.' " To what reality was who
adapting how? Translate this question to the Chinese, the American, the Vietnamese and the Viet Cong views in our current participation in a "*not*-war" and I think you might share with me my
belief that id, ego and superego could well have a field day in this
battle.

If the ego is derived from "cultural norms," among other things,
what are these norms—or today what are the extra-ordinary
stresses? What is the relationship between health and morality
when it evolves under the cloud of atomic warfare and potential
annihilation? What is normal, what is healthy, what is pathologi-
cal when a person by belief and training refuses to pick up arms
and kill, and then is punished for his refusal? Does adequate synthesis, does adequate self-preservation require adaptation to the

reality of the powerful one if rebellion or protest may endanger one's self? Such adaptation could truly be a form of insanity.

I regard the Nazism of Germany as a national psychosis. My view might fit with Dr. McLaughlin's definitions, since the behavior patterns could be seen as resulting from constriction of perceptions and repression of feelings. But what if the argument is raised that it was adapted by some in the service of survival?

Dr. McLaughlin's chapter has important implications for the whole of community psychiatry, group processes, and health through togetherness. I regard community psychiatry as little other than a new social-reform movement, possibly worthwhile if seen as such, but relatively useless as a therapeutic tool that might lead to increasing a person's awareness of his instincts and his conflict and his struggle to harness them. Yet thousands of people will be diagnosed, treated, helped to adapt to a set of norms the value of which has yet to be assessed.

Where does this apply to the hospital? Talbot and Miller, in a recent issue of *Psychiatry*,[2] discuss "The Struggle to Create a Sane Society in the Psychiatric Hospital" and present the problems of appealing to strengths and health in hospitalized persons; "it becomes more clearly defined for all community members what is appropriate behavior in society and what are appropriate revelations in society." Fair enough, but how do we separate ourselves from the value systems, the moral judgments that are involved? Or do we, or can we, or should we?

I agree with Dr. McLaughlin that health itself can be defined at present only in the moment of the time and setting. And yet I keep looking for some constancy in basic value systems, wondering how they come to be and how we use them; for this too is part of psychoanalysis and very much a determinant in our own development, where we must seek to define the meaning, value and process of those norms that mold and determine so much of our humanness.

REFERENCES

1. Center Diary: 12. Center for Study of Democratic Institutions, May-June, 1966, pp. 3-9.
2. Talbot, E., and Miller, S. C.: The struggle to create a sane society in the psychiatric hospital, Psychiatry *29*:(#2) 165-171, May, 1966.

9

The Future of the Private Psychiatric Hospital

Lawrence S. Kubie, MD

Consultant, Research and Training, The Sheppard and Enoch Pratt Hospital, Towson, Maryland, Visiting Professor of Psychiatry, Jefferson Medical College, Philadelphia, Clinical Professor of Psychiatry, University of Maryland School of Medicine, Baltimore

By comparison with outpatient practice, the psychiatric hospital provides a better opportunity to study the patient, regulate the therapeutic program, and observe the processes of illness and its response to therapy. Because of its high ratio of staff to patients, the private hospital has an advantage in developing and maintaining programs of care as models of excellence. Increasing costs are placing the privately funded hospital in financial difficulties and on its Board a heavy responsibility to obtain the funds necessary to expand its vital functions.

I justify a life spent on psychiatry by a deep conviction that, beyond its influence as a therapeutic discipline, it is man's first effort to study scientifically his failures to fulfill his potential greatness. I have a further conviction that the private psychiatric hospital is an indispensable instrument of this effort, because it can study vital aspects of human misery not available in any other institution.

I. Introduction

The future of the private psychiatric hospital can be considered only with the issues that will determine the future of all psychiatric hospitals. Today, all psychiatric hospitals are passing through changes, which, however desirable, will materialize only when we have more men and women to do the job. The rate of increase in the number of fully trained psychiatrists, clinical psychologists, psychiatric social workers, and other aides does not approximate the overall rate of increase in the population as a whole or the numbers of vulnerable younger and older people in the population. At all levels of our social structure, there is a new awareness that psychiatric help is possible and that it can be effective if used early enough and if sufficiently expert. Yet the ratio of professional personnel to informed and articulate need is dropping; and it will continue to drop until we mobilize every available human resource in the community. Such an all-out program implies a general recognition of the universality of the neurotic process and also of its vulnerability to psychotic decompensation. Once we have recognized that the neurotic process is one of the major unsolved problems of human culture, it will no longer be regarded as the exclusive preserve of the medically trained psychiatrist. Instead, the psychiatrist will accept his responsibility to provide full clinical training in psychodiagnosis and psychotherapy to nonmedical behavioral scientists to enable them to work as equals by his side. Only then will it become possible to staff our psychiatric hospitals adequately.

I call the neurotic process a major cultural problem because the neurotogenic deviations from the normal course of human psychological development are universal. Many qualitative and quantitative variables are among them; but these are found in every culture known in depth. They measure the universal failure of all of our cultural instruments, a failure that calls on us to mobilize our every cultural resource. Physicians must play a vital role in this, but never alone.[3, 5-7]

Without meaning to imply that we can always succeed in preventing the decompensation of the neurosis into psychosis, careful studies of the history of the prepsychotic neurosis of the psychotic testify to our failure to treat this early and intensively enough to forestall the graver illness. The price we pay for this neglect is a large share of 800,000 psychiatric beds, to whose care we devote only a small fragment of the medical profession. Twenty thousand psychiatrists out of 200,000 doctors constitute a bare 10%, since many of these devote most of their time to administration, research and teaching. This is all we have with which to combat the major health problem of 200,000,000 people.

Furthermore, while the supply of competently trained personnel is decreasing relative to the increasing need and demand, the psychiatric hospital faces a future in which it must expand the range of its activities and take on many tasks never before considered its responsibility. Such expansion requires increases in space, facilities, personnel and training for new and varied skills. It is easy to say that a hospital must become a treatment center, partly residential, vocational, educational, and recreational; that it must become a therapeutic milieu; that the walls between the hospital and the world must be broken down; that the pathway into and out of the hospital must become simple and natural instead of awesome and terrifying. But to implement it demands a dedication of purpose and, of money, personnel, space and facilities beyond anything yet contemplated.

Even this will not be enough. The psychiatric hospital of the future will be predominantly and primarily a *neurosis treatment center:* partly residential, partly ambulatory, a night-care and day-care center. Attached to it will be an annex for the protection and intensive treatment of those patients whose neuroses have decompensated into psychotic disturbances either during the course of treatment or before they have sought help. This is because spontaneous episodes of psychotic decompensation occur not only during the natural evolution of untreated neuroses but also during the treatment, by any methods, of a certain proportion of all neurotic illnesses. This should not lead to the hasty assumption that a treatment has failed. In some types of illness and personality, psychotic episodes may be necessary for the progress of the treatment itself and for ultimate recovery, although, in the present state of our knowledge, some of these psychotic decompensations do not subsequently recover. This too is inevitable.

Finally, the staff of the future psychiatric treatment centers, each built around a neurosis treatment center as its core and each with an annex for caring for psychotic patients, will consist of men whose training will have begun at the point that the psychiatrist of today reaches only at the end of his training, if at all. Every psychiatrist, psychoanalyst, psychologist, psychiatric social worker, attendant, nurse and occupational and educational aide will have been trained first in the psychopathology of early human life—i.e., in the steps by which the human infant and child become psychologically ill. Training will start with the normal psychological development of the infant and toddler, be followed by work with disturbed childhood, puberty and adolescence, and go on to the neuroses of young adult life. Thus a future psychiatrist and his aides will understand how to relate to and deal with the neurotic process, at all stages of its development, before he is confronted with the psychoses. Elsewhere I have discussed the many reasons why it is essential that we reverse the sequence of training to which only tradition has chained us.[9, 10]

What, then, will the future psychiatric center be? It will be a center for the study of people whose neurotic difficulties block and cripple their lives, for the comparative study of how some remain on this plateau for life, and of how and when and why in others the neurotic process will break down into the variously disorganized states of psychoses. But one cannot understand black without understanding white and all shades of gray. Therefore, it will also be a center for the study of the opposite end of the spectrum. The future neurosis treatment center will illuminate the evolution of illness by studying the evolution of health as well, especially as this is evidenced in the freedom to be creative, the ultimate test of health. The creative potential is as universal in man as the neurotic potential; and the study of the evolving processes, one neurotic and the other creative, and of their interactions must go hand-in-hand. To all of this, the future psychiatric center must be dedicated.

Such goals and changes are easier to describe than to accomplish. We ask ourselves, how do we get there from where we are? Where, indeed, are we? And, especially, how can the private psychiatric hospital become a pioneering pathfinder in these future developments, which is what must happen if it is to survive?

Related to these projected changes and underlying them are many complex socioeconomic problems, involving the future organization of human life in general and of medicine, the fate of vast fortunes and foundations, the distribution of means in the population as a whole, and the ways in which treatment of this kind can be paid for out of funds that will be partly state and community and partly private. This leads us to wonder what role health insurance will play, or the insurance provisions of industry, labor, and government; what health funds will be available for the self-employed as opposed to the man who is employed by a large corporation or government; and of course the future role of Medicare. We cannot cover here all of these complex economic and social problems of medical statesmanship and organization; but we can at least acknowledge their existence before we review the major functions of all psychiatric hospitals.

II. Functions of the Psychiatric Treatment Center

Certain of the traditional functions of the psychiatric hospital are obvious, such as the protection of the patient from self-mutilation and self-destruction, the protection of his family and of society in general. In time, chemotherapeutic and/or physiologic methods may be developed for the restraint and/or dissolution of emotional storms of destructive violence, and of what the law calls "the irresistible impulse," whatever its form. But until repeated investigations have established the extent to which these hypothetical future methods can be trusted, the psychiatric hospital will continue to be an essential instrument of individual and social welfare. Clearly, it would be unrealistic to discard it before any new alternative devices have been tested successfully for several consecutive decades, since it takes that long to evaluate long-term results.

In fact, it will be necessary to conduct follow-up studies on all new methods for many years before any delayed side effects may be applied. Sometimes these newer methods merely eliminate the grossly incapacitating manifestations of illness, while leaving untouched the distortions of personality and the psychopathologic processes that underlie symptomatic behavior.

For instance, a woman had been hospitalized for several years for a florid delusional and hallucinatory psychosis. After massive drug therapy, she made a full symptomatic recovery and was allowed to return home to her husband and four children. After a time, at her urging and in spite of her husband's misgivings, the housekeeper-nurse who had looked after the children during her long illness was dismissed. Slowly, all four children began to develop alarming symptoms: truancy, vagrancy, bedwetting, nocturnal terrors. The distracted young husband then discovered that his wife's paranoid personality had persisted, in spite of the elimination of the florid psychotic symptoms, and was now expressed toward their children and the children's friends. He asked me in tears: "What good does it do to take one patient off the State hospital lists today, if you create four new patients for the future?"

The current use and misuse of tranquilizers afford many examples of how the elimination of symptoms can sometimes mask the inexorable advance of the process of disease, much as the excessive misuse of morphine in past decades would mask the symptoms of an acute appendix until it ruptured, to produce a fatal peritonitis. Psychiatry is not exempt from such risks. Consequently, years of observation of the delayed aftereffects of physiologic, chemical and psychological devices are essential for both the progress of our scientific knowledge and the immediate care of patients. It is extremely difficult if not impossible to carry on such periods of critical and sustained observation without hospital control and protection.

These facts, although elementary and well-known, are often overlooked in the current upsurge of unsophisticated optimism about open methods of handling acute and chronic disturbances. This is particularly true of those who have had least clinical experience, whether in private or public practice and with nonhospitalized or hospitalized patients.

Perhaps it may become possible to serve the needs of our patients and of the community without any psychiatric hospitals at all; but we are far from this possibility today. Nor am I convinced that this will ever happen, nor even that such a change would necessarily be beneficial. The "retreat" has many creative potentials and in different forms is deeply rooted in many cultures. Even prisons can serve as healing retreats for some prisoners, though they make it impossible to rehabilitate others. Similarly, our best hospitals may make certain patients inaccessible to help, even as they aid others and protect society.

The current fashion to think of hospitals as having solely noxious effects is misleading and naive. Isolation from family, friends and work, a bird's-eye view of one's life from a distance, the concentration on therapy in the hospital atmosphere, and many other aspects of hospital life may actually be essential for effective therapy, whether organic, psychological, or both. We have no medicolegal instruments to enforce this: but our patients frequently could benefit from some form of "certification for the facilitation of treatment."

Contrary to current fantasies, the psychiatric center will not disappear, but it will change. Among many changes, it will become part of a complex center for the study of all aspects of human psychological development. The many other useful functions that psychiatric hospitals perform are obvious; but because the current fashion is to dismiss them slightingly, I will restate them.

   1. They make it possible to give a patient that immediate

sense of distance from the inciting situations that only separation in time and space can provide. Such separations can be misused, and often have been; but this should not lead us to overlook their potential value when properly used. The failure to recognize the therapeutic values of separation is reenforcing a general tendency to depreciate the psychiatric hospital and also to assume that patients must necessarily make better progress when they are treated in or close to their own homes. On the contrary, successful treatment sometimes requires the maximal possible distance from base.

For some patients, distance provides a breathing spell without which they cannot bring their problems into focus. For them, the psychiatric hospital can be a magic mountain from which they can survey their problems with a degree of detachment and objectivity that they find impossible when they are in the midst of the turmoils of life. This is true for psychoses and neuroses. We tend to forget that in the early days of psychoanalysis, all roads led not to Rome but to Vienna, Thomas Mann's "Magic Mountain." Vienna was the first European neurosis treatment center of modern times. In this country, we had S. Weir Mitchell in Philadelphia; John George Gehring in Bethel, Maine; then Austen Fox Riggs followed by Robert Knight in Stockbridge, Massachusetts.

2. As the severity of the patient's tensions and disturbance fluctuate, hospitals can adjust the amount of restriction and protection to their needs. During critical phases of treatment, such a daily grading of protective devices can be of maximum importance; yet it is virtually impossible to provide it in extramural practice.

3. The hospital environment can provide a gentler facsimile of the home situations in which the patient became ill. Other patients may constitute surrogates for rival siblings, the administration for parental authority. Problems centering around the relationship between the sexes may be activated by the appropriate use of coeducation on halls, in recreation, and in work programs. The hospital can alternate all-male groups, all-female groups, or mixed groups consisting of age peers or mixed ages. Thus the hospital as a therapeutic milieu can at times be quite neutral. It can deliberately increase or lessen general stresses. Or it may create circumscribed and specific situations of stress that can activate and facilitate treatment and test its progress. In such ways as this, the hospital can so vary the environment in which the patient lives that his problems can be brought into clearer focus for study. To attempt to do this extramurally would be quite impossible without creating at astronomic costs, a miniature hospital around every patient.

4. Many a patient breaks down because he has become caught in a dilemma that, to him, is insoluble, as for instance when a mixture of conscious and unconscious guilts and fears makes it impossible for him to turn either right or left. This is the classical "double bind." In such a dilemma, he may finally explode into an episode of acute psychotic decompensation. Frequently, the hospital rescues him from this dilemma, giving him temporary easement, thus preparing its patient for a gradual return to the outside world, where he can attempt gradually to resolve the dilemma.

5. Again, the hospital can give a patient temporary protection from those specific triggers usually overlooked and unrecognized by the patient himself, and that consequently come to light only in the course of the microscopic study of his life history. Often such precise life histories can be gathered only in the protecting atmosphere of the hospital, as the patient becomes able to explore his life and to communicate about it.

6. Instead of working in the isolation of private or of clinic practice, psychiatrists in a hospital can pool their observations. This provides opportunities to compare theories, techniques, and the influence of personality differences, as these affect the daily handling of patients, their adjustment to the hospital, and their progress in therapy. These opportunities are not always utilized as fully as desirable; but in extramural private practice they are rarely even possible.

7. Finally in a hospital, round-the-clock observations by many trained observers replace the uncontrolled and spotty observations of one man for an hour here and there. Such multiple observations by more than one physician or other therapist, each with his own biases, make it possible to correct the distortions that arise through the bias of any one discipline and of any one observer working alone. Multiple observers at multiple listening posts can compare notes. This alone gives the hospital an enormous advantage in the study of the processes of illness, whether neurotic or psychotic, and in the evaluation of therapeutic progress.

In summary, we can say that for both the neuroses and the psychoses the treatment center, as compared to the relative isolation of ambulatory outpatient practice, provides a better opportunity to study the patient, to observe the illness as a process and also its response to therapy, to regulate and grade the entire therapeutic program, and to integrate theory and practice. The fact that no hospital achieves all of these perfectly is not a reason for discarding the hospital. In the present state of psychiatric knowledge, it continues to be an indispensable if imperfect instrument for the pursuit of these goals.

In theory, all of this should be possible equally in public and private hospitals. In practice, these advantages can be pursued only in limited measure in even the best of our enormous public institutions.

III. Unique Advantages of Private Psychiatric Hospitals

1. As Model for Public Facilities. The late Dr. Alan Gregg used to describe how the presidents of state universities would come to him—as Medical Director then Vice-president of the Rockefeller Foundation—to urge the Foundation not to lessen its support of the privately endowed universities. Their reason was that the private institutions provided the public universities with their best arguments for budgetary needs and educational policies, their most helpful models and standards, and so assisted them in their annual struggles with their legislatures.

2. For Study of Long-term Patient. The private psychiatric hospital fulfills a function indispensable for the progress of psychiatry itself, but which cannot be served by the relatively minute psychiatric wings of general hospitals, or by the limited psychiatric units of the teaching hospitals of our medical schools. This is the intensive study of the long-term patient. The large public hospital serves primarily the practical management of large numbers of patients. After new methods have been tried in smaller research units, it can subject them to mass tests. Because in public hospitals each psychiatrist must take care of too many patients, he cannot explore deeply individual patients and the evolution of their problems and illnesses. Therefore, the large public hospital can contribute relatively little to our understanding of the processes of disease. The small psychiatric unit in general hospitals and in the department of psychiatry of a medical school studies primarily the intensive care of acute disorders and of relatively brief episodes of illness, plus the essentials of psychosomatic medicine. The opportunities to work with patients who require long periods of study and treatment are circumscribed by the limits that must be placed on the duration of hospitalization in such facilities. This leaves the independent private psychiatric hospital as the only place where varied methods of dealing with prolonged psychological illnesses can be studied intensively over long periods and under favorable circumstances. For this very reason, however, the private psychiatric hospital should not yield to the temptation to focus exclusively on the patient whose illness is sudden and brief. If it does so, it will turn its back on the very area to which it can make its unique contribution. It is not generally appreciated that the study of the long-term patient is one of the most difficult and important aspects of psychiatry. Let me try to make clear why this is so.

The neurotic process starts early in life, as a deviation in the development of two vital aspects of human psychology: *1*. the interrelationship between preconscious processing and conscious sampling under the influence of unconscious conflicts, and *2*. the relation of affects to their originating sources. When these double dissociations occur, i.e. between the symbol and its roots and the affects and their origins, the chain reaction of the neurotic process is launched.

This chain reaction is marked by the production of symptomatic behavior, which may be transient or persistent, and by developmental arrests of "fixations." Both the symptoms and the arrests have many serious secondary consequences, which give rise to new distortions in further development, which feed back further consequences, and so on. When the therapist attacks this chain of reverberating reactions, he usually must attempt first to eliminate or ameliorate the immediately crippling symptoms. After this comes the long slow task of trying to make possible the belated processes of growth and maturation that had been blocked in childhood by the neurotic process itself. But growth takes time, which must be measured in months and years, not in days and weeks. This is perhaps the most important and the most difficult task that the psychiatrist undertakes. It cannot be rushed by any verbal formulae or any chemical or physiologic devices, although these can be of value in lessening the distorting and obstructing influences of the symptoms.

This is why the persistent study of the long-term patient, in a setting that provides him with ample space to move around, not merely a ward or room in a general hospital, is essential for the maturation of both the patient and the psychiatrist. As I have written elsewhere,[8] our possible rate of development as psychiatrists is limited by the rate at which our patients change. It is only by interacting as participant observers with their ups and downs over months and years that we can achieve our own clinical and human maturity. Today the only setting in which this can occur is the private psychiatric hospital.

3. For Comparison of Different Methods. Optimal conditions of care are essential for precise evaluation of new methods. It has long been known that in the overcrowded understaffed public institution, almost any change introduced seems for a time to produce prompt improvements, as in the old epileptic colonies. Such was seen in the initial naive overoptimism about psychoanalysis, insulin, metrazol, ECT, and "modern" chemotherapy. Consequently, to draw definitive conclusions about the action of any new drug or of any new therapeutic maneuver from a study conducted solely in large public hospitals is dangerous. Innovations—psychological, physiologic or pharmacologic—must first be tested on patients who can be observed intensively by many observers and who are being cared for under optimal circumstances. Otherwise, it is impossible to isolate the effects of the innovation from the effects of other concurrent variables. Therefore, the small psychiatric pavilion, where tests can be made on acute cases, and the large private hospital, for tests on long-term cases, provide together an indispensable setting for the definitive initial testing of new therapeutic methods. Mass testing comes later in the large public institutions.

4. For Community Integration. The path to closer integration of the mental hospital with the community and its resources can best be charted and demonstrated by the private hospital. For the patient, the path back to health involves such things as education and reeducation, vocational retraining and reemployment, sheltered workshops and special recreational clubs, the education of the home and of the community, and the development of special types of "half-way houses" or "friendly homes" for patients who are ready to leave the hospital but not to return to the homes and occupations in which they became ill. In the use and development of such occupational and community resources, the public hospital can be loosely integrated with the network of other public agencies. This is as it should be. But the enormous numbers of patients and often their limited educational backgrounds and vocational potentials put impossible burdens on agencies with equally limited funds and personnel. Therefore, in these as in so many other areas, the private psychiatric hospital must do the pioneering, exploring and testing, thus guiding the larger public institutions to the large-scale development that follows.

5. For Research and Training. The private psychiatric hospital must lead the way for the large public institutions in training, in research and in overall service to the families of patients and to the community as a whole. In all of these the private hospital has indispensable advantages over the public hospital, outpatient practice or private practice. I will list here a few of the opportunities:

a. to make careful follow-up studies, so as to evaluate and compare therapeutic results on long-term cases.

b. to compare different techniques with comparable groups of patients, and to compare the responses of different groups of patients to the same technique.

c. to organize selected groups of patients for contrasts of many kinds. This implies the right to select patients for the kinds of problems they present, a right that no public institution can have.

For all of these, an enlarged professional staff is needed (nurses, attendants, social workers, psychologists and psychiatrists), backed by an increased budget. Therefore, the ratio of staff to patients must constantly increase [2,4] as in all hospitals that contribute to the progress of medicine. Yet this fact usually surprises the layman, especially the lay members of a Board of Trustees. Quite naturally, they expect scientific and technical advances to reduce operating and professional labor costs. Their model is the effect of automation on labor costs in industry. For many reasons, this model is invalid for both somatic medicine and psychiatry.

None of the special functions of the private psychiatric hospital is possible unless it has a high ratio of professional staff to patients. Achieving this ratio involves recruiting more men and women from all the behavioral sciences, and drawing back into hospital psychiatry senior clinicians with many years of experience in private and clinic practice. The hospital that is growing into scientific maturity must hold onto a selected group of its own able and experienced graduates. Without them, neither its clinical work nor its research can be mature, nor will it be able to recruit able young aspirants. Young men with ambition and high standards will not come to an institution whose ladder of advancement is cut off at an arbitrary point by a policy of scattering its best young graduates.

An increasing ratio of staff to patients is one of the best indexes of the quality of a private psychiatric hospital, and of whether it is meeting its scientific, medical, educational and social responsibilities. Here the psychiatric hospital resembles any fine medical school, which also holds on to many of the best of its trainees. The danger of inbreeding is checked when these are invited to other schools and hospitals, and when a policy obtains of bringing in men from other centers. Growth should never come from one's own graduates alone; yet a school or private hospital that feeds all its graduates to other hospitals and centers is dissipating its best strength.

Another cause can be unwise economies by a lay board. It is possible to hold on to the best among the older men only when the funds available for salaries grow constantly. Even when a large initial endowment exists, it is imperative to conduct campaigns to raise new money, which some Boards are reluctant to undertake. They fail to recognize that funds are a responsibility to both science and the community, and also that such campaigns, instead of alienating the community (as some fear), draw the hospital and the community closer together.

Whatever the reason offered for reluctance of the lay Board to seek new funds, their failure to do so will in the end deprive a hospital of its primary source of strength—namely, a growing staff of men of increasing maturity. Without them, the hospital becomes a ladder that has a few rungs at the bottom and a few at the top but nothing in between. Such hospitals die. Strength in a hospital is secure only if the ladder is intact.

IV. The Problem of Survival

In 1944, the late Alan Gregg read a paper on "The Future of the Voluntary Hospital," [1] at the celebration of the 100th Anniversary of the founding of the Butler Hospital in Providence, Rhode Island. With characteristic tact, Dr. Gregg pointed out the path that the private psychiatric hospital will have to follow if it is to survive in the modern world. Retrospectively, it is clear that if his advice had been heeded, a fine old hospital would not have closed its doors.

He emphasized that the private hospital must provide services that cannot be provided by any other psychiatric facility and that are needed by a numerically limited and financially privileged clientele and the community.

He then considered how changing values affect future planning, pointing out that the voluntary hospitals must always be ahead of tax-supported institutions, and that in order to be ahead they must change their legal structure so that they can "survive on government subsidy and yet remain autonomous enough to satisfy their trustees and administrators." He indicated that if they are to merge their findings with general medical knowledge, the privately endowed hospitals must also be integrated into the stream of medical education (as very few are even today; Appendix A) and that they must be integrated into the regional needs for medical care in their respective communities (See Appendix B). Finally, he warned that unless private psychiatric hospitals will fit into such a framework, even hospital insurance could only "delay their final failure and not prevent their eventual breakdown." This brings us to the financial problems that lie ahead.

THE FINANCIAL SQUEEZE

The following general statements about trends are based on statistics furnished by ten representative private psychiatric hospitals. Their methods of gathering data varied, and the data were not uniform. Nevertheless, these cautious generalizations reflect these trends because they conform to the experience of the majority.

Private psychiatric hospitals face increasing financial problems, consequences of a wide application of lessons learned from private psychiatric hospitals in the past.

1. Effects of the Shift from Acute to Chronic Cases. By observing the operation of private psychiatric hospitals, general hospitals have learned how to operate small psychiatric pavilions. This is making it possible for general hospitals to take care of many of the transient psychotic upsets that used to come directly to the private psychiatric hospital, and that contributed to their financial security.

Until recently, few medical schools had their own provisions for psychiatric care. Medical students were "taught" by taking them to visit the nearest state psychiatric hospital for demonstrations of psychotic patients. Today, medical schools have developed large departments of psychiatry and their own pavilions for the care of acute cases, of relatively fewer intermediate cases, and of still fewer long-term cases.

A strong trend exists to treat in private offices and outpatient clinics many patients who in the past would have been hospitalized at once. This is partly sound, but based also, in part, on naive optimism.

None of these new developments provides for the study and care of the long-drawn-out cases that have always been cared for in public and private psychiatric hospitals.

For obvious reasons, the facilities that care for brief and intermediate cases threaten the financial security of private psychiatric hospitals. When an illness is limited, the resources of patients and families from middle-income groups can usually pay full rates; but they cannot pay the same rates for longer illnesses. The families of such patients are fearful of running out of funds before the patients have recovered, and may remove patients from any hospital before it is medically wise to do so, or may transfer patients to public hospitals.

Because in the past acute cases were important to the economy of the private psychiatric hospital, the tendency to take care of them in other ways and in other facilities threatens the economic basis of the private hospitals. The shift in the population of private hospitals to a higher percentage of chronic cases tends further to reduce hospital income by slowing up the overall rate of admissions and the rate of turnover.

The same shift produces a misleading impression that patients in private hospitals are not getting well as quickly as they did formerly, whereas in fact the private hospitals are caring for a differently weighted sample of the range of mental illness, which represents a lower proportion of transient illnesses. Many studies of the therapeutic process (whether of the effects of drugs or of psychotherapy) purport to show that new therapeutic methods have yielded no improvements. They neglect to take into account this population shift.

The small, private sanitarium for a quick turnover of weekend drunks is slowly disappearing, as this service is being provided by the small psychiatric wards in general hospitals. The failure to develop adequate medicolegal instruments to make it possible to hold such patients for the long-term hospitalization that adequate treatment would require makes them unavailable to the private psychiatric hospitals that are set up for long-term care of this kind.

2. *The Effects of the Increasing Treatment of Adolescents.* The increasing emphasis on the treatment of adolescents marks an important psychiatric advance, because it means that psychodiagnosis and psychotherapy are being used earlier to prevent grave later developments, i.e. before psychological illness has had time to take its full toll. Yet this population shift can also threaten the economic welfare of the private psychiatric hospital.

The care of the adolescent requires specially trained personnel and educational and occupational facilities appropriate to this younger group. Sometimes, these are custom-made to meet the varied ages, sizes and needs of different young people of both sexes, all of which is expensive. The young parents of young patients are rarely affluent; the younger the parents, the more difficult it is for them to meet the costs of private care. Finally, at the end of an adolescent's long and costly road to health, the resources of these parents will have become even more depleted, leaving them with little to contribute to the hospital's future endowment. Consequently, the trend toward earlier treatment is affecting adversely not only the current operating income of the private hospital, but also the prospects of future fund-raising from grateful ex-patients or their parents.

3. *The Influence of Longevity.* In seeking a solution to this problem, many hope that the care of increasing numbers of older patients will balance some of these financial difficulties. It is true that as more individuals live into the later decades, the numbers of older patients must increase. It is true also that these increasing numbers of older people are living longer; and that they are surviving in relatively good physical health for longer years, while medicine is passing through a transitional era in which it cannot yet maintain them in equally sound mental health. At the same time, automation and the population explosion is decreasing the relative span of the *earning years* of the average healthy adult. Consequently, the average adult wage earner from the middle-income group faces a decreasing span of earning years with an increasing load of young and old unemployable dependents, i.e. both in adolescence and in old age. (This of course is the basic reason why pooling the costs of this through a system of social security has become an inescapable necessity). Yet it is the domi-

nant middle-income group that the private hospitals have always served in the past and on whom they have depended. Now as a consequence of these changes in population, longevity, life-expectancy, and automation, fewer members of this group are able to carry the expense of prolonged private care for the increasing numbers of their unemployable aging and surviving dependents. The older citizens cannot be looked to to solve the financial problems of the private psychiatric hospital.

It is not yet possible for the administrators of private psychiatric hospitals to predict the extent to which in coming decades social security, company pension plans, union plans, and health insurance (individual, group or national, voluntary or compulsory) or Medicare can fill this increasing economic void.

It should be obvious to the Boards of Trustees of all private psychiatric hospitals that their hospitals cannot survive solely on income from past endowments plus income from current patients. This realization places squarely on the Boards the responsibility to raise the additional funds imperative to the continued existence of the private psychiatric hospital.

V. The Sin of Operating in the Black

These facts force the conclusion that the private psychiatric hospital should never expect to operate in the black. Morally, it should not try, for trying would sacrifice the activities that are its contribution to society, the advance of psychiatry, and the care and treatment of its patients. To operate in the black is a public confession that it is failing to perform these functions. Moreover, if any private psychiatric hospital were to operate in the black, it would at once be in danger of losing all government and foundation support and its tax-exempt status. Even from a mercenary point of view, then, to operate in the black is shortsighted.

If, on the contrary, the private hospital seeks constantly to expand its vital functions, it will become a pilot plant, with ever-increasing investments of space, personnel and money, in the intensive study and care of the few. Its choice of patients will depend on not whether they can pay, but what it can do for them, what can be learned about psychiatry by working with them, and what can be taught to others through this experience.

It will select a fair share of its patients because of the nature of their illnesses and the scientific challenges with which these confront the staff, irrespective of financial status. It will do this for the purpose of teaching and testing new methods. The endowed psychiatric hospital that selects its patients in this way has a moral and legal right to call on available public funds, local and national, and on all interested private foundations. And it will *have* to call on its community, because until all local sources of private funds are mobilized, it will find it hard to raise money elsewhere.

The endowed psychiatric hospital will have to enter into contractual arrangements with schools and colleges, public and private, insurance companies, labor unions and industry, because it will need financial and moral support from these groups. Furthermore, it must draw its patients from the whole community if it is to study illness as it occurs in all elements of society.

One further implication: no hospital restricts its patients to one faith or color. Only a few still restrict their staff. The day has passed for the sectarian or segregated *hospital* and for the segregated or sectarian Board of Trustees. If private psychiatric hospitals are to win the community support on which their survival depends, their Boards of Trustees must represent not only finance, law, the churches, industry and education, but labor as well. They must represent every race, creed and color in the community. They must look less like the Union League and more like America.

APPENDIX A

RELATION OF PRIVATE PSYCHIATRIC HOSPITAL TO MEDICAL SCHOOLS AND PRIVATE PRACTITIONER

FUTURE DEVELOPMENTS will necessitate *a.* a closer relationship to medical schools, *b.* an opportunity for those training in medical schools to expand their experience, by periods of integrated work in private psychiatric hospitals, and *c.* an opportunity for those working in private hospitals to receive certain training in psychiatric teaching units in medical schools. Such experience for both groups will produce men trained and experienced in both phases of psychiatry. The interchange is essential for upper echelons and those at the level of residency training. Staff appointments to private hospitals, therefore, should equal the status of teaching appointments in medical schools. Accepting an appointment to the staff of a private psychiatric hospital would not then endanger a man's position on the ladder of academic advancement, and would rid psychiatry of anomalous discrepancies in prestige between the two. (A like rivalry existed between the "Universitäts Psychiater" and the "Anstalts Psychiater" of 19th Century Germany.)

Such an interchange would be of advantage to both. It would make available to the private hospital more men with scientific and academic aspirations, and thus improve the caliber of the personnel of the private psychiatric hospital. It would bring the clinical sophistication of private hospital practice to that special brand of naivete that characterizes much medical school psychiatry, hopefully ending what has aptly but unhappily been called the era of the "academic amateur." At present, greater clinical knowledge and experience is found in the staff of the private hospital; yet prestige and status cling to the psychiatrists of medical schools. The ensuing sterility for both should not continue.

If the private hospital is to draw fully on the resources of the community, it will turn to both the community's social and educational agencies and its private practitioners of psychiatry. A movement will then start towards the open staff as the basic organization of private hospital practices. Patients, families, and private practitioner need this continuity. They accept a hospital through relationships made outside it, and when patients enter it, these ties cannot be terminated without endangering their confidence. The outside psychiatrist needs this continuity because his own full maturity of experience requires an opportunity to follow the course of illness both within and out of the hospital. The hospital psychiatrist wants the continuity because he too needs to know psychiatry from the point of view of the family and community. Indeed, with group practice developing on the outside and with the hospital becoming a neurosis treatment center, we can look forward to a systematic interchange of staffs as an essential part of the training of all of us.

Therefore, it is to the mutual advantage of practitioner and private hospital to move in the direction of the open staff: for the private hospital to develop a relationship to private practitioners that gives them an active role and a share of responsibility in the hospital. Private practitioners will benefit the hospital by their criticisms of traditional hospital procedures. At the same time, the influence of the hospital will expand when it makes many of its special resources available to the ambulatory patients of the private practitioner—for instance, the occupational and educational resources. The hospital's facilities could be made available for the organization of joint social clubs for hospital patients, discharged patients and patients of private practitioners, thus helping to solve the social needs of all.

Furthermore, as the preventive uses of psychiatry increase, the private psychiatric hospital will develop more as a residential treatment center for children, adolescents and neurotics in general. Its integration with pediatricians and with pediatric psychiatry will then also increase.

APPENDIX B

RELATION OF PRIVATE PSYCHIATRIC HOSPITAL TO NATION, STATE, COMMUNITY

FACILITIES FOR THE CARE of psychiatric illnesses are developing all over the country. A consequence is that to an increasing extent every private hospital is turning towards its own community—its own city, county, state, and perhaps a few nearby states. Formerly a large percentage of the patients of the better known psychiatric hospitals came from remote states or distant countries. While this still occurs today, in most hospitals the percentage of patients from distant areas is gradually decreasing. For this practical reason, as well as many others, private psychiatric hospitals will find themselves becoming agencies of the communities in which they exist, merging the services they provide with those of other facilities in the same areas.

This community-centered evolution will create problems, but will also have many compensating advantages. In general, it will mean a breaking-down of the ancient Chinese wall between the "asylum" and the community. It will make it possible for the private psychiatric hospital to conduct more careful social investigations of home conditions and better follow-up studies; to provide—for the supervision of patients still under treatment but on their way to discharge—friendly halfway homes and temporary foster homes, varied types of home care, and day-hospital and night-hospital; to open its facilities to outpatients; and to treat family groups in several different ways.

Such services would always have been useful, but neither people nor psychiatry was ready for them, nor could they be provided for patients from long distances. Since they could not be made available to all patients, and since they are costly of time, personnel and money, there was a tendency not to develop them at all. Now, however, they have become essential.

These developments will require additional space, equipment, and professional staff who will bring to the work more complex and varied training. The necessary increases in hospital budgets will be the responsibility of the nation, state, and community; because the private psychiatric hospital will be serving along with its state and community, science and the country as a whole.

For APPENDIX C—RELATION OF PRIVATE PSYCHIATRIC HOSPITAL TO ADOLESCENT PATIENTS—*please see page 241.*

REFERENCES

1. Gregg, A.: The future of the voluntary hospital, Rhode Island Med J *27:*381-436, 1944.

2. Kubie, L. S.: Research in psychiatry is starving to death, Science *116:* 239-243, 1952.

3. ———: The pros and cons of a new profession: a doctorate in medical psychology, Texas Rep Biol Med *12:*692-737, 1954.

4. ———: An institute for basic research in psychiatry, Bull Menninger Clin *20:*281-287, 1956.

5. ———: The need for a new subdiscipline in the medical profession, Arch Neurol and Psychiat *78:*283-293, 1957.

6. ———: Social forces and the neurotic process, chap. 3, *in* Leighton, Alexander H., ed.: Explorations in Social Psychiatry, vol. 128, New York, Basic, 1959, pp. 65-80.

7. ———: Is preventive psychiatry possible? Daedalus *88:*646-668, 1959. Japanese Trans; US Information Agency, Pub Americana, 1960.

8. ———: Editorial: The maturation of psychiatrists or the time that changes take, J Nerv Ment Dis *135:*286-288, 1962.

9. ———: Traditionalism in psychiatry, J Nerv Ment Dis *139:*6-19, 1964.

10. ———: Reflections on training, Psychoanal Forum *1:*96-100, 1966.

Discussion

ROBERT W. GIBSON, MD

Medical Director, The Sheppard and Enoch Pratt Hospital,
Towson, Maryland

WHEN I SAW THAT THE title of Dr. Kubie's chapter was "The Future of the Private Psychiatric Hospital," I immediately made myself the discussant, for a particular reason. I have always been fascinated by a certain type of movie. A man is walking along the street; he discovers a little alley that he has never noticed before; he walks along this alley to a newspaper booth. He picks up the newspaper and begins to read; and to his astonishment it is next week's newspaper. He then reads about the stock market and with no effort whatsoever makes his fortune.

I hoped that I was getting "next week's paper" on private hospitals and that this would make us successful here at Sheppard without any effort. After reading Dr. Kubie's chapter, I realize that he has given me no help whatsoever toward avoiding effort. It is not a prediction of things to come: he has told us what the private psychiatric hospital *should* be, not what it *will* be.

I was reminded of my first meeting with Dr. Kubie, when he defined his role here at Sheppard as that of a gadfly. A gadfly is an annoying or provoking person, especially one who stimulates or provokes to activity and especially at the analysis and defense of idea by persistent criticism. I do not think that there are many of you who would seriously question Larry's self-definition, either in this chapter or in his relationship to psychiatry. I have to tell just one story about my personal encounter with his gadfly role. A few years ago I went into one of those fits of desperation that hospital administrators have when both the world and certain patients seem to be against them. I rather summarily tossed out the ringleaders of a rebellion against the hospital policies. I promptly got from Dr. Kubie a little treatise, entitled "Ruminations on Boom

200

Lowering and Other Hospital Ceremonials." I do not think I need tell you what was in it, but I should tell you that Dr. Kubie helped: he organized and participated very actively in a number of discussions where we attempted to identify some of the problems that were leading to the issues of the moment. Thus, Dr. Kubie does himself a disservice when he says he is a gadfly. I am more inclined to think that he is an idealist, even though I suspect he will not admit to that.

I am particularly pleased to see his stress on the need for hospitalization for certain patients: the stress on the need for good hospitals. Nowadays it seems fashionable to say we should get rid of hospitals. Occasionally this seems so exaggerated that the worst public health menace in the country seems to be the psychiatric hospital. Dr. Kubie pinpointed very well the indication for hospitalization and the values. He has also emphasized, and I am very much in accord, the importance of the medical staff to the hospital: building a sound staff, attracting men, and helping them to stay. I think we should not overlook the contributions made by other personnel: of our over 500 employees here at Sheppard, only about 40 are physicians. Dr. Kubie showed some of his idealism as he described what a hospital must do beyond its direct services: how it should aspire to lead the way.

I cannot stir up much controversy, except perhaps in one area. Dr. Kubie spoke of the financial squeeze and the hard road that is ahead of us. Some four years ago I was attending a meeting of private psychiatric hospitals, and there was a certain uneasiness at the meeting. Everyone wanted to know how your census was holding up, were you losing money this year, and so forth. This group was concerned as they looked toward the future. But at a meeting of this same group this past year, the tone was completely different. On all sides we heard about new things that were being done, beautiful architectural drawings of new hospitals were displayed, and men were at the meeting to find out how to start new hospitals. The whole atmosphere was different; the future seemed brighter than ever. There is no longer the concern that units in general hospitals will be competitors or will make it difficult for the private psychiatric hospital to survive. These units have helped identify psychiatric problems earlier, and they have now become one of our largest sources of referral. Rather than being a threat to us, they are of great assistance.

Dr. Kubie touched on the question of insurance coverage. I find that about 70% to 90% of the patients entering most psychiatric hospitals have some kind of insurance coverage and these coverages are broadening all the time. Medicare has been mentioned but we will not know for some time how it will work out. It provides very liberal coverage, and I hope that it will spur the private insurance groups to extend their coverage.

For many years, about 2% to 3% of the psychiatric beds in this country have been in private hospitals, although they handled about 20% of the first admissions. If the support of financing expands as I predict, it is possible that we may see a significant increase in the number of private hospitals, their size and number of beds. If the percentage were to move up to say 5%, 6%, or 7%, we might see a day when as many as half of the first admissions go to private hospitals. At this point I feel convinced that we are going to see the expansion, elaboration, and overall improvement in private-hospital psychiatry.

10

Old Wine in New Bottles
Superego as a Structuring of Roles

JOSEPH O. CHASSELL, PhD, MD

Senior Psychiatrist, Austen Riggs Center, Incorporated,
Stockbridge, Massachusetts

In his original formulation, Freud traced the origin of the super-
ego to the "overcoming of the Oedipus Complex." This concept
attributed conscience, rigidity and self-punishment to uncon-
scious processes and was later used as an overall explanation for
socialization. These older concepts are no longer adequate. Mod-
ern role theory offers a better explanation for the child's gradual
assimilation of experience leading to socialization and the devel-
opment of a persisting sense of self-identity.

WHEN I FIRST READ FREUD'S *Das Ich und Das Es* [4] in 1926, I was so excited that I boasted to my skeptical psychologist friends that psychoanalysis was not merely a patchy empirical-theoretical approach to certain mental disorders, but now presented a coherent general theory of personality. It took into account as *It* (das Es) original nature, drives (Triebe, not Instincts—a concept in bad repute among psychologists), 'I' or Ego as the growing, learning person, and the Uber-Ich (the over-I, above-I or -self, later translated the superego), which referred to conscience and its unconscious determinants. This brilliant and ingenious structural theory seemed, and I think was, a great advance. Old concepts took a new meaning; Ucs, Pcs, Cs became descriptive qualities. Unfortunately, the general rule that forms of thought change slowly held in the specific case of psychoanalysts: the Self or Ego remained a secondary object of study, the Id (as it was later called) became pretty much a synonym for the good old mythological Unconscious—the prime object of study—and the superego on the one hand remained tied to Freud's original genetic derivation and on the other became a vague catchall for inhibiting and constricting influences. Thus the situation stood, aside from some pioneering that was considered a bit suspect (e.g. Alexander, Sullivan, Fromm, Horney, Kardiner), until Hartmann and his associates focused more attention on the ego, its study became "psychoanalytic," and "ego-psychology" was born.

How adequate are the 1923 conceptual tools for encompassing the new data and delineating the various "structures" that may be said to constitute the personality? Here I shall limit my discussion to the superego. My thesis is that it is a replaceable concept, and I am emboldened by the considered formulation of that brilliant psychoanalytic theorist, the late David Rapaport [11]:

> The concepts of structure and relative autonomy (Hartmann) are indispensable to the theory, and at present it is not possible to foresee changes in the theory which would eliminate them. But the concepts of id, ego, superego, and the differentiation of the ego into defense-, control-, and means-structures are neither as indispensable to nor as independent from the theory.

I.

The superego concept, as Freud originally defined it, was too narrowly based and tied to a specific theory of its development. I remind you that he started with delusions of being observed, and mused [5]:

> How would it be if these insane people were right, if in each of us there is present in his ego an agency like this which observes and threatens to punish. . . ? Ever since, under the powerful impression of this clinical picture, I formed the idea that the separation of the observing agency from the rest of the ego might be a regular feature of the ego's structure, that idea has never left me. . . . (Standard Edition 22:59.)

In its origin, he granted certain precursors via identification— often with the beloved mother—one ego becoming like another "not unsuitably compared with the oral, cannibalistic incorporation of the other person" (SE 22:63), and in case the object is lost or given up, setting that person up in one's ego—compensating by identifying. But the superego is only established in full strength and development with the abandonment of the Oedipus complex. Without this normative crisis, there would be no proper superego. And later influences

> regularly make important contributions to the formation of character; but in that case they only affect the ego, they no longer influence the superego, which has been determined by the earliest parental imagos. (SE *22:*64.)

Socialization is almost inescapably traumatic to the immature ego, for

> In the space of a few years the little primitive creature must turn into a civilized human being; he must pass through an immensely long stretch of human cultural development in an almost uncannily abbreviated form. This is made possible by hereditary disposition; but it can almost never be achieved without the additional help of upbringing, of parental influence, which, as a precursor of the superego, restricts the ego's activity by prohibitions and punishments, and encourages or compels the setting up of repressions.[6] (SE *23:*185.) *

But since Freud believed that civilization demanded such upbringing, with a resultant severity of superego, and since the resolution of the biologic oedipal tie also required a fateful renunciation, he could see the superego as an essential part of the normal personality, rather than as a particular pathologic product (or even as a kind of transference repetition compulsion). He could proclaim: "Where id was, there shall ego be," but not "Where superego is, there shall ego be."

> Fear of the superego should normally never cease, since, in the form of moral anxiety, it is indispensable in social relations, and only in the rarest cases can an individual become independent of human society. (SE *22:*88.)

The genius of Freud's restless mind, however, did not let him stop at unsatisfactory formulations. In the *New Introductory Lectures* he could say:

> I cannot tell you as much as I should like about the metamorphosis of the parental relationship into the superego, partly . . .

* It is instructive to note the similarity of this formulation with that of Freud's contemporary, Emile Durkheim, whose *Education Morale* expresses the same philosophy of socialization. See Piaget, *The Moral Judgment of the Child.* chap. 4.[10]

because we ourselves do not feel sure that we understand it completely. (SE 22:63.)

In his final writing on the subject (*The Outline*), he was still wrestling with it. According to his custom, he turned back to the bedrock of his basic theories, saying, "The superego is in fact the heir to the Oedipus Complex and is only established after that complex has been disposed of" (SE 23:205), and then going on to a widened neo-Freudian extension:

> Throughout later life it [superego] represents the influence of a person's childhood, of the care and education given him by his parents and of his dependence on them—a childhood which is prolonged so greatly in human beings by a family life in common. And in all this it is not only the personal qualities of these parents that is making itself felt, but also everything that has a determining effect on them themselves, the tastes and standards of the social class in which they lived and the innate dispositions and traditions of the race from which they sprang. (SE 23:205-206.)

He even ventures to suppose that his schematic picture of the psychical apparatus may apply as well to the higher animals that resemble man mentally:

> A superego must be presumed to be present wherever, as is the case with man, there is a long period of dependence in childhood. . . . Animal psychology has not yet taken in hand the interesting problem which is here presented. (SE 23:147.)

Did he mean that the ethologists should investigate the passing of the Oedipus complex in primates? Or was he now referring not so much to the superego as narrowly conceived, but rather to the whole process of primary-group socialization? Did he mean to include under superego the language a child learns, which does so much to structure his forms of thought and his conception of his environment, usually ascribed to the ego? Talcott Parsons maintains that while Freud was focusing on individual psychology, he was moving logically toward sociological considerations.*

---

* Parsons, indeed, attempts to use the superego as a bridge between Freud's theory of personality and the analysis of culture and the social system (Superego and theory of social systems, *Psychiatry* 15:15-25 (Feb), 1952 [8]; also Social structure and the development of personality, *Psychiatry* 21:321–340 (Nov), 1958.[9]) But curiously, so far as my reading of Parsons' further writings goes, he does not find this narrow bridge useful.

As it now stands, then, the concept is most ambiguous, referring on the one hand to a narrowly delineated, specifically derived, separate agency in the mind, "determined by the earliest parental imagos," and on the other to the complex processes and structures implied in socialization.

Could the concept then be simply discarded (except, of course as a descriptive term for certain pathologic clinical conditions)? Social psychologists are increasingly prone to pay verbal respect to it, and then to rely on other tools. Most current research, such as that at NIMH, uses role-theory, with object relations being seen in terms of role-ascriptions, learnings, delineations, reciprocal roles, whether symmetrical or complementary.

Psychoanalysts themselves are finding difficulties. Joseph Sandler, attempting a classification of superego material, writes that the therapists

> have preferred to sort their clinical material in terms of object relationships, ego activities, and the transference, rather than in terms of the participation of the superego.
>
> The very process of examining the superego in detail in order to clarify it has blurred it to some extent, at any rate from the point of view of theoretical lucidity and simplicity. . . . In a sense the superego has thus lost some of its theoretical identity as a compact and coherent organization, as a thing-in-itself and an agency in the production of psychic conflict.*

In our case conferences at Riggs, as indexed by Mrs. Ida Mower

---

* Joseph Sandler, On the Concept of the Superego, 1960.[12] He and his associates at the Hampstead Child Therapy Clinic have perservered in the effort to achieve a coherent research concept, which may be examined in detail in subsequent studies: cf. The Classification of Superego Material, 1962.[13] More recent is *The Hampstead Psychoanalytic Index,* by John Bolland, Joseph Sandler, *et al.*[15] This gives an explanation of the general categories used, and illustrates with the material of a child of three. Perhaps it is because of this illustrative purpose that a chapter about this young child is headed "Superego." As I read it, all the data in these papers could have been fitted more functionally into various schemata of role-situations and responses. In fact, the headings tend in that direction: relation to authority outer and inner, projection onto substitute authorities and similar object relations. (This rich material might well be used as a scanning test on alternative hypotheses.)

The troubled searching in the Freudian text for precise rubrics is eloquently recounted in the Hampstead Group's paper, The Ego Ideal and the Ideal Self, 1963,[14] and we may well wonder if they may in the end find themselves evolving a more empirical classification.

over a period of years, superego is used sparingly, and as nearly as I can judge, it almost never appears in the original Freudian package. As another test, I have examined Erikson's *Young Man Luther*—presumably a gold mine for harsh superego—and again my impression is that while Erikson occasionally uses "superego" in a somewhat global sense, his actual conceptual working tools are essentially different.[2]

Before we turn to alternative formulations and possibly more useful concepts, we can still be intrigued by the processes that led Freud first to postulate his narrow delineation of superego and to hold to its oedipal derivation throughout his life. It can reasonably be hypothesized that Freud noticed a new stage of structuring or internalizing of parental norms *coincidental* with the oedipal phenomena he was studying, and drew a causal relation between them. An alternative sequence can be drawn from the direct child-observation researches of Piaget, on intellectual as well as moral judgment. His Stage Two seems to occur at around ages four to six, but applies to a myriad of phenomena hardly subsumable under superego: notions of causation, of the external world, the rules of games, ideas of justice, and the like. Flavell summarizes [3]:

> There appear to be two moralities in childhood, at least within the culture from which Piaget's subjects were drawn. The developmentally earlier one is a *morality of constraint,* formed in the context of the unilateral relations between child as inferior and adult as superior. The child adapts to the prohibitions and sanctions handed down from on high by reifying them (a *moral realism* akin to the *intellectual realism* studied earlier) into moral absolutes—simple "givens" which are unquestioned and sacred, in theory if not in practice. Hence the child views wrongdoing in objective rather than subjective terms, is confined to the letter rather than the spirit of the law, and is incapable of seeing morality-relevant acts either in terms of the inner motives of the actor or in terms of the social-interpersonal meaning of the act itself. . . . With development, this morality of constraint is at least partially replaced by a *morality of cooperation.* . . . Both morality and logic are fired in the crucible of the spontaneous give and take, the interplay of thought and action, which takes place in peer-peer interactions. . . . It is only through a sharing of perspectives with equals—at first other children, and later, as the child grows up, adults—that a genuine logic and morality can replace an ego-centric, logical, and moral realism.

This change begins to take place about the time a child is mature enough to spend part of his day away from his mother, and although he is still prone to turn frequently to his substitute mother, usually the teacher, he normally does not cling to her skirt, and he is showing a keen interest in his peers. Three processes naturally follow:

1. Intrigued and challenged by this new stimulation, the child first responds with the only schemata he knows: the intellectual and moral realism learned at home. To the extent that he is insecure, he tends to cling to it, and it becomes rigidified; otherwise he is open to new experience.

2. In this widening world of childhood he begins to realize that there are other families and other ways, and it is brought home to him that he has a last name and belongs to a particular family that has its own 'membership character,' which may again become a rigid defense.

3. As he dares move out and become a member of a peer group, he becomes immersed in the fascinating activities of the so-called 'latency period' and moves partially out of the orbit of the parental solar system. Normatively, he is *pulled* by the aliment (to borrow from Piaget) that feeds and satisfies his maturing capacities, rather than being *driven* by his ocdipal disappointments.

Could it be that Freud interwove these concurrent phenomena with the dependent-erotic concerns of his anxious and inhibited cases, and drew the wrong causal conclusions, viz., that the pathologic internalization of the family norms was due to having to give up objects, rather than being in fear of moving outwards? I believe so.

II.

Freud derived socialization, as we have seen, primarily through the process of identification based partly on love for the mother and partly on fear of the father as well as a wish to be like him. Freud acknowledged his dissatisfaction with this exposition (SE 22:63), and I would venture the reason was that his clinical material provided information only from later infancy when processes have become more complicated—after all, Freud's "identification" presupposes both a self and a person object. Earlier structuring of the response and perceptual system would be classified better as empathy and role-learning.*

Empathy, or affective-gestural communication, I do not see as incorporation or identification out of love. It is based on "sign stimuli" or "social releasers" † setting off unlearned instinctual responses, rather than "symbols." The infant held by its mother during a London air-raid "catches" her responses of fear—i.e., it involuntarily defines the situation in terms of the cues she gives; if she is not holding it, or has it on a pillow, it does not so define it. Now this may be based on dependency, but not on love, at this stage; it is part of the biologic need to orient the organism to the environment (cf. Pavlov).

> It so happens that we recently acquired a spaniel pup. She has become quite attached to my wife, who feeds and cherishes her. She is very hostile to our old setter and barks viciously when the setter approaches my wife; there is no love lost between them. But when they are out of doors, she apprentices herself to the older dog: is this looming donkey an enemy to be approached cautiously and barked at, or a friend to fawn upon and tease? Setter is not alarmed, so why bark? But is it a strange car approaching? Setter barks hysterically and spaniel goes into spasms of excitement, ready for flight or attack. After all, one wants to know the "scoop" about how things are organized around here, an eager-beaver apprentice operates on the principle, "Nothing ventured, nothing learned." Such is the basic stuff of empathy. The puppy and the baby do not respond to complicated inner images of the good or bad mother—at least at this stage—but they are experiencing and learning how to define the situation in terms of the "appropriate" response, which is selected from a

---

* (This latter concept, in its main developments, comes from George H. Mead, a coeval or predecessor of Freud in these matters—the late nineties— and I shall be borrowing from him at intervals.)

Logically, but tediously, I should mention the first steps, or prestages, of socialization, as outlined in the first three stages in Piaget's *Growth of Intelligence in Children* (Internat Univ Press, 1952), and occupying the period until about the seventh month when, as Spitz persuasively demonstrates (Rene Spitz: *The First Year of Life*, Internat Univ Press, 1965), the mother is selected out from a multiplicity of experiences and becomes a unified object. But to do so would take us into reflex-responses, canalization, possibly imprinting, innate release mechanisms, reinforcement, and the like. Let us take all that for granted and start with Empathy.

† N. Tinbergen, *The Study of Instinct,* Oxford, 1951, pp. 76 and 171.

galaxy of available reactions by "sign stimuli," among which are cues from others in the pack.

A maltese poodle we once had came around the corner into the kitchen and found confronting him on his own level a big green watermelon. He instantly reared back, growled, circled and barked, then sniffed (emergency reaction to natural sign of the unknown, possibly dangerous). If I, as the established leader of his pack, had taken this object as an opossum or porcupine and backed away, the cue would have helped select the natural sign of danger and he would have continued to circle and bark. But I went up and petted the melon, and he approached and sniffed it (Animal, mineral or vegetable? Vegetable!). He had learned to define this situation by experiencing its salient elements: the pack-leader responds without fear, I find it to be a vegetable; that's life. Next time poodle bumps into melon there will be a whiff of danger, but it fades away as he perceives the situation as previously experienced.

We now have the anlage of Role, if not actually its early stages; the leader, the follower, the definition of the situation with the help of cues and empathy.* "Significant symbols" in the form of words—more precisely, sounds—also play a part.

In 1937, I participated in an episode that made as strong an impression on me as the spool game did on Freud:

When one of my daughters was approximately two, we acquired a kitten. My daughter discovered an entertaining pastime—to gather up the kitten, take it to the cellar stairs and pitch it down. The only way we could seem to deter her from this mayhem was to slap her hands and say "No, no" as simultaneously with the act as possible. Shortly thereafter, the kitten invaded the breakfast table. I pushed it off with one uninhibited sweep of the arm.

* Empathy as species-specific cues—not imitation, but responding to cues for structuring or releasing action: The resident male cat makes passes at the young puppy. She is puzzled at first—how to take this (the way a baby looks bewildered when first being made over by uncle or grandfather). Then she gets the signal: "This is play; what's the game?" So far, so good; some sort of gestural communication has been set up. But they belong to different species: he plays like a grown cat, she plays like a puppy, and the game is disrupted. After innumerable daily trials they finally settle on a form of play that both can comprehend: they chase each other, but they do not get into the tusseling, pummeling, pseudo-biting that would be natural to two cats or two dogs. After three months, they progress a bit further: the dog acts like a wrestler, the cat like a boxer. They still don't identify, although they can anticipate the other's role performance.

My little toddler rushed up to me indignantly, slapped my hand and said, "No, no!"

This is as simple a case of empathic role-learning as I can find: when someone throws a kitten, someone else indignantly slaps the hand and says, No, no! In 1939, I observed a slightly more complex incident:

> A faculty colleague and his wife came to dinner, bringing their three-year-old daughter, of whom they were embarrassed because of her proneness to masturbate. During the meal, she dawdled, keeping at least one hand in her lap. Her parents were polite, but one could see them casting reproving glances at her. She brought the offending hand from under the table, slapped it with the other hand; most probably she muttered "Naughty," but this I cannot vouch for.

Here was the child's behavior being role-defined as bad by the parents, but the expected punishment was being withheld. She knew what came next, and did it to herself. In this case, it seems to me, there is some perception of the disapproving attitudes of the parents toward herself, she is taking the role of the other, the relationship is now "internalized," and one can now say that she "identified."

But I am arguing that identification is not essential to the structuring of roles; there need to be only experience in learning how people act and cues how to react, and this is learned just as other natural phenomena are learned. To quote T. Newcomb (*Social Psychology,* Dryden, 1950):

> One of the most important psychological changes occurring at this stage is that of acquiring musts and must-nots—i.e., the child's taking on, as his own motivated behaviors, fixed ways in which things should or should not be done. From the adult point of view the child may seem very capricious in his musts or must-nots. By no means all of them correspond to adult rights and wrongs. . . . Having little understanding of the rationale of the rules, the child accepts them as part of the universe—like the law of gravity, which he also does not understand. They become incorporated into his social motive patterns just as the judging of distances becomes incorporated into his motive patterns for jumping. . . . Other persons are as they are and do as they do for the same reasons that sticks and stones, the sun and the moon, are as they are. . . . (p. 305)

The ways in which an individual takes his roles are determined by his perceptions of self-other relationships. Self-perceptions are first acquired in relation to household intimates, and role behaviors based upon them are quite persistent. (p. 370)

As identification increases, but is still incomplete, the results can be quite comical or pathetic:

> I must have been taught sexual modesty at an early age. When approximately four, we went to see my father teaching. There he sat at ease, surrounded by an interested class. But he had his legs loosely crossed, with one hand dangling between them. I was embarrassed for him and had a strong impulse to go up and whisper in his ear that he should not do that—obviously he did not know the right way to act.
>
> A few months later, I felt equally embarrassed for my mother: we were entertaining at supper the local school superintendent and a visiting educational dignitary. In the course of the meal, the latter asked for water and my mother poured it into his already emptied milk glass. She made a flustered apology and went for another glass. He naturally passed it off as a matter of no consequence, but I knew that a terrible *gaffe* had been committed, and I could see no way to repair the humiliation.

Summarizing the processes illustrated in these four vignettes, we see that the child does not simply react; he responds within a perceptual field that embraces the whole experience, including how he comprehends the attitudes of the other actors. *He experiences, within his limits, the whole drama.* So when someone else goofs or is not "hep" he knows how it should go, and can take the role of the elder. It's as simple as that. Watch the small child talking to its doll as it puts it to bed or takes it to the bathroom. What soothings or injunctions does it use? Those that any three-year-old in his local culture knows are the words to use on a baby. Or watch a somewhat older child who doesn't "know" how to do the dishes at home but is taking over the task temporarily of baby-sitter to younger children: what expertness she displays in organizing them for the dishwashing ritual!

The vignettes cited have all been from the phase of moral (and intellectual) realism or absolutism.* Under usual conditions, as

* I can remember, during the same age period from which I drew my own two examples of role-learning and participation, watching men digging and laying a water line, with fire hydrants. Soon afterwards it rained, and I peered earnestly up at the sky to see the hole where God had turned on the

Piaget has shown,[10] this moral realism yields to the influence of experience with peers and becomes moral relativism (other kids in other localities play marbles according to different rules; one learns that these rules are "right" for that neighborhood and one must play according to them). But if the moral absolutism has been reinforced so that it continues as a rigid structure of perception and action, then at least in that area learning stops or is blocked. The reinforcement may be by strong imposition of inhibitory responses—great fear instilled at the violation of taboos, e.g., or anxiety at being ostracized from love and group membership. This would come closest to the Freudian "superego," especially when the sanction is threatened castration in the boy or conviction that one has been castrated in the girl. But such a rigid structure can also obtain when there has been little acculturation, as in an isolated tribe or a group-isolated religious sect. Margaret Mead has described the personal breakdown that can afflict an individual from such a tribal culture when he goes out into another world, and Western literature is full of literary accounts of such vicissitudes. But when the structure is so rigid that no new role-taking can occur without destruction of the sense of ego-continuity, that is, the basic or core self-others conceptions, then we have psychopathology in one form or another.

Now, am I correct in classing these phenomena under the heading of structuring of roles? *"Role . . .* refers to the behavioral consistencies on the part of one person as he contributes to a more or less stable relationship with one or more others." (Newcomb, Turner, Converse: *Social Psychology,* 1965.) There are ascribed "positions," such as boy, girl, baby, grandfather, that are defined by the reference group in terms of its cultural norms so that, in effect, the ascribed position contains a role prescription: "Little

hydrant and was spraying us—an example of *intellectual realism.* Even at age six or seven, when we went to visit the Lyons I could not get over an uncanny feeling that they would not be like other people.

Moral realism likewise is characterized by a kind of strict literalism. Rules are 'given,' sacred and untouchable, in the nature of things. Piaget found that the child, if questioned, assumed that they had been made by father, grandfather, or God. If the interlocutor suggests playing marbles another way, he is repulsed by remarks such as, "It isn't right; it's against the rules; it ought to be played *this* way." The rules are literal because there is yet no sense of the spirit of the law, or its intent. So if a child were to break 15 cups, accidentally, he should be punished more than if he broke just one cup while trying to reach the jam put out of reach on an upper shelf.

boys don't cry," "Babies are adorable no matter what they do," "Grandfather has time to play with you." There are role demands: "You are old enough to dress yourself," and achieved roles: "He is president of the student council and our most responsible young citizen." Out of his multiple responses, inner and outer, in each role-relationship, and out of the multiple responses of the significant others, grows a coherent role definition, a role-conception, role performance, and an accruing concept of oneself in relation to the others, and later the generalized Other.* Such definitions of role start even before the child can take them in: "Oh, what a good baby," croons the beaming mother as she unpins a dry diaper, or—if it is wet—"Oh, dear, what a nuisance you are; will you never learn?" Even the most naturalistic physical explorations can be loaded with pieces of role-definition. Well do I remember at an early age tentatively touching the top of the kitchen stove: there was pain and little blisters rose on the tip of each finger. I don't remember the outcome, but presume that I was comforted, buttered, and warned. But it could have been otherwise: "It served you right; I told you to keep away from that stove; you can't be trusted out of sight. Now *you mind!*"—using the natural phenomenon as a punishment reinforcement for the role of dependent obedience, and at the same time imposing on me the image of a culprit. Watch any overprotective mother strolling with her run-about: "Don't walk on that wall, you might fall and hurt yourself," "Don't play there, you will get all dirty." Depending on temperament and previous experience, the child may become timid and clinging, or irrepressible and heedless, as if acting on the premise: "She is always picking on me; I might as well do as I please."

To conclude this section, then, we have seen that there is utterly crucial role-learning going on in the early years, and that this results in basic or core self-others conceptions in which the conception of self, including the meaning of one's own feelings and physical capacities and appearance, is imbedded in the total transaction or experience, so that one is learning the 'roles' of others simultaneously with definitions of one's own role or roles. We have seen

* Such coherence assumes consistency from the reference group. If there is chaos, with one behavior rewarded one minute and punished the next, or if nothing that one does seems right, then quite naturally there could develop an apparent lack of "conscience" and utter confusion what one is, i.e., no structured role system.

that this primary structuring of the ego, the perceptual field and the drives, is "first acquired in relation to household intimates, and . . . [is] quite persistent," and that it may be quite uninfluencable, having "been determined by the earliest parental imagos." But we also have seen that in a young child, such a structure may normally be characterized as moral realism; that when it remains such, it does not permit adaptation, and that psychopathology may result (perhaps not if the culture remains an unchanged unity). We may conclude that the Freudian "super-ego" represents a special, and pathogenic, case of such inculcated rigidity, and as such is not an inherent part of the "anatomy of the mental personality" but rather an artifact and a disabling deformity to the extent that it impedes growth or learning. Several patients of mine have survived into chronological adulthood with such complete moral realism, reinforced by frightened dependence on parents, that they could never really experience the give and take of peer relations, and as adult patients retreated in panic from the very thought of participating in a therapy group.

The Core-Self, the closest to a center, a Who I am, is based on primary role-relationships, the mutual definition and mutual regulation as reached in the basic trust and autonomy normative crises as described by Erikson. Where this has been violently imprinted or distorted, we have the basis for an Interactive or Transference Character Disorder, since "transference" is the other pole of internalized role relationships, the primary "reference-relationship." *

Or, to put it more constructively, we can think, in place of *das Ich, das Über-Ich*, and *das Es*, of the *Organism* and its needs, and—following G. H. Mead—the *I* and the *Me*. The *I* is the person in action (i.e., living), and as such is a changing, homeostatic equilibrium. As Mead says, "It is only after we have acted that we know what we have done; it is only after we have spoken that we know what we have said." [7] But what we do or say, while always new, is structured by the *Me*, the Self, the Self-Others Role learnings that have made up our experience—and in turn is assimilated into that structure. The *Me* is that global frame of reference—of

---

* To push these ideas a step further, it becomes evident that characteristics such as Passivity, Masochism, Aggressiveness are not just "traits" of the individual, but are responses to an internalized role-relation, involving an internalized (transference) object; and most, if not all, defenses are directed at persons or images, including the image of the self (the ego-ideal).

self, or others, of past, present, and future—the landscape or "field" in which the I behaves, usually according to well-established 'habits' but sometimes impulsively, to its own surprise.*

Conclusion

The 1923 formulation of the superego was an important step in psychoanalytic psychology, bringing into focus mental structures always implied but not spelled out in the eager exploration of psychosexual development, and in relating conscience, rigidity, and self-punishment to unconscious processes. But the concept was originally delimited to a narrow spectrum of phenomena, and was tied to a specific theory of origin. Later, it was broadened to include virtually the whole of socialization, even though Freud clung to the last to its specific derivation. My conclusion is that the Freudian superego describes a particular pathologic and culture-bound special variety of role-complementarity, and that Freud attributed its establishment at the time of the "overcoming of the Oedipus complex" to what he observed in his clinical material, viz., that children who were fixed in a state of moral realism by their peculiarly strong ties to their parents were unable to pass on to moral relativism, and remained bound by the moral realism of the superego.

This, today is not the most productive conceptual formulation. It does not lend itself to the researches of social psychologists; it makes serious difficulties for psychoanalytic research into detailed phenomena of childhood; clinical case conferences can largely dispense with it; and even literary reconstructive case studies need not depend on it.

Now we find that primary group role-learning is the present best formulation. Role-learning covers Freud's original phenomena—the inner voice, the rigidity, the demands, the guilt, the self-blame, the harshness (and, I might add, the corruptibility). Role theory does not presume that this structure reflects accurately the true attitudes of the parents, but represents the child's assimilation of experience, colored by his own drives and needs, perhaps especially his security needs.

The concept of role-learning includes all gradations of socializa-

* Mention of the word "habit" establishes a contact with John Dewey's *Human Nature and Conduct*,[1] which, published in 1922, already conceptualized most of the issues we grapple with.

tion, from the so-called precursors of the superego, through the phases of moral realism, into moral relativism and social norms by way of peer interactions and experiences in the secondary groups of society. It does not imply that a patchwork of variegated roles is all that there is to a person. Under usual developmental conditions, it would include a core-self or sense of persisting self-identity, a Basic Personality Structure (Kardiner), or an "inner gyroscope."

REFERENCES

1. Dewey, J.: Human Nature and Conduct, New York, Holt, 1922.

2. Erikson, E. H.: Young Man Luther, A Study in Psychoanalysis and History, New York, Norton, 1958.

3. Flavell, J. H.: The Developmental Psychology of Jean Piaget, New York, Van Nostrand, 1963, pp. 295 f.

4. Freud, S.: Das Ich Und Das Es, 1923, trans. as The Ego and the Id, *in* The Standard Edition of the Complete Psychological Works of Sigmund Freud, vol. 19, London, Hogarth Press.

5. ———: New Introductory Lectures, 1933, Standard Edition, vol. 22.

6. ———: An Outline of Psychoanalysis, 1940, Standard Edition, vol. 23.

7. Mead, G. H.: Mind, Self and Society, Chicago, Univ Chicago Press, 1934, p. 196.

8. Parsons, T.: Superego and theory of social systems, Psychiatry *15*:15-25, 1952.

9. ———: Social structure and the development of personality, Psychiatry *21*:321-340, 1958.

10. Piaget, J.: The Development of Moral Judgment in the Child, London, Kegan Paul, 1932.

11. Rapaport, D.: The structure of psychoanalytic theory: A systematizing attempt, Psychol Issues *2*:(#2)128, 1960.

12. Sandler, J.: On the concept of the superego, Psychoanal Stud Child *15*:128-162, 1960.

13. ———: The classification of superego material, Psychoanal Stud Child *17*:107-127, 1962.

14. ———, et al.: The ego ideal and the ideal self, Psychoanal Stud Child *18*:139-158, 1963.

15. ———, et al.: The Hampstead Psychoanalytic Index, New York, Internat Univ Press, 1965.

Discussion

Sarah S. Tower, MD

*Private practice of Psychiatry and Psychoanalysis, Associate Professor
of Psychiatry, The Johns Hopkins University School of Medicine,
Baltimore*

My thanks to dr. chassell for recalling to me my first reading of
The Ego and the Id and the illumination that comes, especially
when one is young, with concepts that order our experience. His
"old wine," I take it, is the concepts of psychic structure advanced
by Freud in 1923, which we found so heady, and of these particularly the concept of the Superego. His thesis is that this is a replaceable concept. He proposes that the concept "superego" be
replaced by a concept of "primary group role-learning," which
seems to be the "structuring of roles" of his title. Role-learning, he
says, covers Freud's original phenomena—the inner voice, the
rigidity, the demands, the guilt, the self-blame, the harshness, and
the corruptibility. And Dr. Chassell offers a series of vignettes
from daily life, human and animal, to illustrate the applicability
of role-learning concepts to behavior exhibiting some of these
phenomena.

My concern is not whether the phenomena listed can be ordered
by a concept other than that of the superego. They have long been
ordered by other concepts—for example by a concept of God and
the devil struggling for the human soul, which has served more
persons in more diverse ways than either of the concepts under
consideration is likely ever to do. Nor is my concern even whether
another concept would lend itself better to the researches of social
psychologists than the concept superego. My concern is this: If
Freud's concept of psychic structure called superego be replaced
by a concept of "structuring of roles," what will be accomplished
thereby for theory development in psychoanalysis?

In science, concepts are the product of observation, and in turn

219

become part of the methodology of further investigation. The methodology determines what concepts will become available by observation. In Dr. Chassell's vignettes, the method and the material are, respectively, direct observation of behavior in a situation, either immediate or in recall. This methodology will neither produce the associatively structured, predominantly verbal material of a psychoanalysis nor permit of the lengthy, detailed participant observation that permits exploration of the depths of the mind. Without such access, the spectrum of conscious-unconscious mental functioning, with its dynamic and economic aspects, can hardly be explored. Since these modes of observation and the concepts resulting therefrom are basic to structural theory in psychoanalysis and, indeed, to analytic theory in general, an observational approach that cannot yield and does not use these conceptual tools and which does not stimulate further investigation in these areas, cannot be considered centrally useful in psychoanalysis.

I regret that clinical psychiatry in general and psychoanalysis in particular have developed largely independently of the basic academic science of psychology, and undertook to discuss Dr. Chassell's chapter partly in hope of rapprochement now, and of cross-fertilization of ideas. Yet such cross-fertilization comes only as differring basic modes or designs for study, and the resultant bodies of concept are utilized for their capacity to complement and stimulate rather than to replace. That the theories of the various social sciences and of psychoanalysis can be richly fertilizing reciprocally has been sufficiently demonstrated, in the one direction in such works of Freud as *Totem and Taboo,* and in the other direction in the work of present scholars such as Talcott Parsons. Moreover, the techniques of direct observation, given something of the duration and detail of an analysis, are the only means now available to extrapolate the understandings and insights of psychoanalysis back across the preverbal years, and the returns as recorded in the studies of Spitz and many others can leave no doubt of the usefulness of such complementarity. The outcome of complementarity is, then, not a rebottling of old wine, but a new product, a broadened and deepened body of concept and theory, or even a whole new perspective.

For these reasons, therefore, I cannot concur in the proposal to replace the concept "superego" with a concept of primary group role-learning, but look, rather, to the continued mutual complementing of two diverse modes of investigation.

Several aspects of Dr. Chassell's paper invite comment: first, "the Freudian Superego," that sum of Freud's experience with his own superego and of his observations of his patients, but especially the former as it comes through in Dr. Chassell's quotation from *The New Introductory Lectures* of 1933. This Freudian superego must be sharply discriminated from the concept superego as it stands now, having been worked over from 1923 to the present, and I will cite only Dr. Jacobson's 1964 monograph *The Self and the Object World,* Part II, "Superego Formation and the Period of Latency." I would like also to discuss with him the phenomenon of cultural lag in superego development having to do with its generally repressed state, which makes both for conflict between the generations and for continuity in, for example, such deep-laid values as the expectations of autonomy that underlie a people's readiness for autocratic or for democratic institutions. Or the balance of moral realism and relativism in people at large. And I would like to discuss progressive obsolescence in the particularities of individual superegos, especially in periods of rapid cultural change. All the superegos of Freud's generation are now gone, and probably those of most of his patients, and such a superego in this time would likely make for stress between the individual and his culture, and, perhaps as Dr. Chassell points out, for pathology. Dr. Chassell's and my superegos, laid down in the opening decades of this century before two world wars and the great depression, before the explosions of atomic bombs and of populations, before the explorations of space, will soon be gone, and those and other new cultural circumstances will be reflected in somewhat differing superegos.

This, in itself, will necessitate continuing investigation of the phenomena subsumed under the concept Superego. And in this investigation, I hope and expect that social psychologist and psychoanalyst will continue, each with his own methodology, their fruitful collaboration.

REFERENCES

1. Freud, S.: Totem and Taboo, Standard Edition, vol. 13, London, Hogarth Press, 1913, pp. 1-162.
2. ———: New Introductory Lectures on Psycho-analysis, Standard Edition, vol. 22, London, Hogarth Press, 1933, pp. 1-182.
3. Jacobson, E.: The Self and the Object World, New York, Internat Univ Press, 1964, 250 pp.

11

Narcissism: Benign and Malignant Forms

EDITH V. WEIGERT, MD

*Private Practice of Psychoanalysis, Chevy Chase, Maryland,
Chairman of the Faculty, Washington School of Psychiatry*

*Ego weakness corresponds to malignant, or negative secondary,
narcissism, and is characterized by efforts to escape from frustration by repression, distortion and denial. Such negative secondary narcissism is at the core of psychiatric maladjustments. The
objective state of ego development in positive secondary narcissism is approximated by self-esteem. During psychoanalytic
treatment, a meaningful relationship is gradually crystallized out
of the distortions of transference-countertransference reactions
caused by defenses against anxiety, hatred and rage. In this
transition from unconscious primary narcissism to a preconsciously controlled benign secondary narcissism, forces of spontaneous generosity are freed, leading to a trusting mutuality in
interpersonal relationships.*

FREUD'S CONCEPT OF NARCISSISM, which he introduced into psychoanalytic theory in 1914,[8] widened horizons, particularly the study
of the major psychoses. These Freud differentiated, as the "narcissistic neuroses," from the "transference neuroses"—hysteria,
phobia and obsessive-compulsive neurosis—with which Freud and
his followers were then more familiar. Later studies in schizophrenia in this country—by, to name only local authorities, Frieda
Fromm-Reichmann, Harry Stack Sullivan, Lewis Hill, Otto Will
and Harold Searles—demonstrated that the transference of conflicts into the doctor-patient relation is not missing in schizophrenia. Rather, it is intensified, since the existence of the whole
personality of the schizophrenic patient is threatened by conflicts
that mobilize aggressive impulses to the intensity of destructive-

222

ness. Self-love turns into self-hatred, and a benign narcissism—which, with self-interest, aims at preserving the individual existence—turns into the malignant narcissism of self-destruction. Narcissistic defenses, particularly those of a negative malignant kind, offer the greatest resistance to psychoanalytic therapy.

Narcissism was seen originally as an intermediary stage of development between autoerotism and object libido. In the transference neuroses, the aggressive impulses are often masked and mitigated by libidinal impulses. The major psychoses did not lend themselves to treatment and exploration by a private practitioner, since these patients are mostly hospitalized, and a Jewish physician, like Freud in antisemitic Austria, had no access to leading positions in municipal and academic institutions. Therefore, Freud conducted his studies mostly with neurotic patients and had to fall back on the autobiographical notes of Schreber for a more detailed study of the paranoid form of schizophrenia. Had he seen more psychotic patients, he might have isolated the aggressive from the libidinal drives earlier. Originally, he assumed that the libidinal instincts are opposed to the instincts of self-preservation and lend themselves less to the build-up of human solidarity than the instincts of self-preservation. In his earlier studies, the aggressive instincts were defined as sadomasochistic partial components of the libidinal drives, which are directed against the instincts of self-preservation. After the introduction of narcissism, Freud's instinct theory became centered on the dualism of Eros and Thanatos, libidinal versus aggressive drives. According to his *Beyond the Pleasure Principle*,[9] the preservation of individual as well as communal existence depends on the preponderance of Eros over Thanatos.

When the psychoanalytic ego psychology, on the basis of Sigmund and Anna Freud's writings,[10,7] was elaborated,[11,6,17] a sharper differentiation between primary and secondary narcissism emerged, which marks the transition from the pleasure-pain principle to the reality principle in human development. What had been called [1] the preambivalent phase of libido development became the phase of primary ego autonomy, where the aims of ego and id are still harmoniously intertwined. Magaret Mahler [15] has distinguished a phase of early autism, and a later phase of symbiosis between mother and infant followed by a phase of separation and individuation. A prolonged symbiosis or a return to autistic withdrawal interferes with the development of a benign secondary narcissism.

Balint [2] has called the phase of primary narcissism a phase of primary love, although it seems to me an adultomorphic interpretation to call the infant's automatic responses to maternal care expressions of love, just as Melanie Klein's [14] concepts of an early paranoid and depressive position appear to me as adultomorphic interpretations of infantile behavior. It has been suggested that we "drop the primary-secondary narcissism and replace it by the general term narcissism, since actually, we are dealing only with what was called secondary narcissism." [4] I agree that primary narcissism is a physiologic stimulus-response rather than a psychological phenomenon. The infant continues to some degree the "embeddedness" (Schachtel [20]) of the maternal womb. The infant's helplessness and dependency on maternal care makes the boundaries fluid. Against overstimulation, he is protected by the stimulus barrier. He responds to the mother's hope, trust and loving care with well-being and the unfolding of his potentialities of growth, which imply the promise of trust, hope and love in his further development.

This symbiosis lasts longer in human beings than in all animals that start an earlier independence from parental care. In animals, on the other hand, preservation of the individual and of the species dovetails on the level of instinctive regulations of stimulus and response throughout the life span. Conflicts arise in animals, in life situations and laboratory experiments, but they are solved on a preconscious level, as they remain preconscious in early stages of human development. The ethologists describe such instinctive conflict solutions: When in a pack of wolves a conflict about supremacy breaks out, the rivals fight till the weaker gives in. He submits his jugular vein by a turn of his head to the teeth of the victor in a gesture of humility, but the victor does not bite. Such instinctive reactions are directed towards the preservation of the individual as well as of the species.

In early human infancy, the cry of distress is not yet a cry of anxiety. The infant is protected by a stimulus barrier even against contamination with the anxieties of the mother. In a highly disturbed mother-infant relation reported in my practice, the nearly psychotic mother was tormented by doubts of her maternal competence. She might drop the baby and break his neck or suffocate him in the feeding process. The infant responded to the flood of agitated stimuli automatically by stopping nursing and bottle-feeding completely, at the age of six weeks. The mother's alarm escalated. Fortunately, the infant had not yet developed object constancy and ego identity. This baby recovered from his hunger strike, which automatically protected him from being flooded by the mother's ambivalent emotions by permitting him calm and un-conflicted nursing care in a hospital. At a later stage of the child's development at home, with awakening consciousness the maternal anxiety and the child's defenses against it created severe conflicts of ambivalence also in the child.

The human infant, like the animal, is bewildered by contradic-tory stimuli, but is not yet anxious. Anxiety is an emotional signal. Emotional signals bring instinctual aims closer to awareness. They arouse preconscious reactions and consciousness, which tend to preserve and organize memories of the past and to anticipate fu-ture pleasures and pains. Instincts in Freud's definition have sources, objects and aims, but only the sources remain uncon-scious. Aims and objects become more and more a matter of choice. They are lighted by flashes of emotional signals and, there-with, submitted to transiently conscious or preconscious censoring decisions. These decisions gradually etablish the nuclei of ego identity and object constancy. At eight months, the signal of genu-ine anxiety, the clinging preference for the familiar person, the recoiling from the stranger are observed. When the child begins to say "I," he is no longer part of the mother or the mothering person, but an *I* over against a *you*. The gradually awakening consciousness has been called by Hegel [12] an "unhappy conscious-ness," because consciousness arouses conflicts that call for decisions. The conflicts are between the *I* and the *you*, as well as between past and future, being and becoming. The two-year-old child fre-quently goes through a period of saying "no" to almost everything that the parent proposes. He wants to be himself, to do it himself, leave the past behind; and he clings still to the familiarity of the past yet reaches out for the uncertain future with a mixture of joyful curiosity and painful anxiety.

The harmony of trust, hope and love experienced in the symbiosis of mother and child remains an aspiration throughout the life span. Emotions signalize the approximation to or the distantiation from this goal. What Rado [16] calls the welfare emo-tions—hope, joy, happiness, tenderness, love and gratitude—sig-nalize the approximation to this gratifying goal of harmony. The signals of anxiety, doubt, anger, rage, hatred, shame and guilt indicate the danger of disharmony and conflict. These emotional signals mobilize the weapons of defense to control the emergency. But often the excess of mobilizing emotions fails to control the emergency; disorganized fight and flight reactions lead to emergency discontrol. They automatically blot out the unbearable aspect of the conflict by repression, distortion and denial, which impair the mastery of emergency.

Freud [9] has denied a drive for perfection in human beings. He saw the human determined by the unconscious energies of his contradictory drives, his constitutional endowment and the contingencies of fate that reality imposes on him. He saw human conflicts arising from the unruly unconscious drives, libido versus self-preservation, narcissism versus object libido, Eros versus Thanatos, and these drives in conflict with reality. It seems to me that conflicts, in animals or the early infant, are more smoothly solved on the unconscious level. The awakening of consciousness creates conflicts, since consciousness demands decisions. According to Sartre,[19] man is condemned to be free in his choices of objects and aims. Once the child has left the unconscious paradise of trusting symbiosis, he is confronted with decisions. He wants to become himself, Sartre's pour-soi; he wants to master his destiny in spite of dependencies and contingencies, and he also wants to become what the other one—in the child's case, the parent—wants him to be, Sartre's pour-autrui. The child needs, before all, the constancy of being accepted. In his emotional conflicts, he often sacrifices the (for him) inferior value of pleasure gain or pain-avoidance for the (for him) high value of object constancy and ego identity. But object constancy is not permanent, and ego identity is in a flux of becoming. Once the child has left the comforting symbiosis, he feels forever incomplete. He is only transiently satisfied with what he has received or achieved, and he reaches out for ever new aims and objects. Ives Hendrick [13] has introduced a drive toward mastery, and Robert W. White [21] a drive for efficacy and competence. But mastery, efficacy, competence are goals, not sources of drive energy. In the transition from primary to secondary narcissism, from the pleasure-pain principle to the reality principle, the goals of instinctual drives become increasingly complex and encompassing through the processes of sublimation.

According to Heinz Hartmann,[11] the primary autonomous functions of the ego extend into a secondary autonomy by neutralization, disinstinctualization of the libidinal as well as the aggressive drives. Hartmann speaks of desexualization as well as de-aggressivation. But the process of sublimation does not imply a quantitative, diminution of drive energy. The change of goals is not only inhibiting, it broadens the activation of drive energies in the service of an expanding ego. Expansion takes place on the biologic level by growth and development and on the interpersonal level by increasing object constancy and consolidation of ego identity. Successful sublimations are the basis for a benign narcissism, which never arrives at homeostasis, but in more and more encompassing integrations transcends the here-and-now situation as well as the regressive trend toward autistic or symbiotic withdrawal.

The child that Freud described in *Beyond the Pleasure Principle* [9] who was distressed by his mother's departure, achieved a successful sublimation. He transcended his distress by inventing the play with the thread-reel, which, in the wish for mastery, he could throw away and retrieve, reassuring himself, therewith, that the departed mother could also be retrieved. The child's confidence in the mother's return is reinforced by self-confidence, since he himself can maintain the image of the good mother who returns over against the image of the bad mother who disappears and deserts him. In the phase of differentiation and individuation, which corresponds to the phase of anal erotism, the child learns to distinguish good from evil. In the earlier oral phase, he is still protected by the unconscious stimulus barrier in the fold of primary narcissism or primary love. Now he learns to decide for himself how to preserve what serves him best, how to reject what is dead and bad. He learns to endure frustration, to postpone gratifications; he learns by trial and error and achieves his early sublimations that guarantee his growing independence and a balanced interdependence with others.

The precondition for successful sublimations is the preponderance of Eros over Thanatos in the antagonistic and synergistic play of drive energies. The danger signal of anxiety mobilizes aggressive as well as libidinal energies in the defense of the ego. As long as Eros prevails over Thanatos, an optimal state of defense, which we shall call courage, can be maintained even under the most trying circumstances. The emergency can be controlled when the individual can transcend the danger that he faces, squarely and with a heightened sense of integration and competence. Danger may arise from untamed drives that send out emotional signals of alarm, or from an unmanageable reality situation, or from a failure of ego functions.

Freud called this failure of the integrating ego functions *death instinct*. But is it an instinct or a failure of aggressive and libidinal instincts to unite and maintain the goal of life preservation, individual as well as communal life? Death is not the greatest of evils when one can face it with courage, but conscious awareness of danger may intensify anxious emotions to a degree that ego functions fall into disarray. Rado [16] called this disarray "emergency discontrol." Brain damage arouses incapacitating catastrophic panic reactions when it does not wipe out consciousness. The drowning person can more easily be saved when he becomes unconscious than when he fiercely but inappropriately struggles for survival. A person who is overwhelmed by depressive, desperate emotions may consciously decide to end it all and, in Bibring's [3] words, let the ego die; yet at the peak of an emergency, the goal of survival may rise from the preconscious to the conscious and take the lead in restoring the will to live. On the other hand, a less serious suicide attempt may accidentally lead to death due to emotional discontrol in a state of disorganizing panic. Consciousness is not always the best guardian of survival and does not always achieve the most satisfactory conflict solutions, since emotions that reach the preconscious and conscious levels as signals for decision may falsify the assessment of reality. Emotions have the tendency to return to magic wish fulfillment and magic denial of adversity, as we see in the dream. Deep sleep is dreamless and permits the relaxation into unconsciousness. Memories of recent or past conflicts stir up emotions that solve the conflicts with the omnipotent magic of narcissism, but when this magic of omnipotent wishes fails, owing to the severity of conflict, the dreamer awakes in terror, overwhelmed by the emotions of helplessness and powerlessness. Also in waking life, the individual who feels incompetent to make decisions and to solve his conflicts is lured by his emotions into short-circuit, magic solutions of regressive, more or less autistic or symbiotic phantasies. When the omnipotence of these magic solutions fails, the individual can become a victim of emergency emotions of anxiety, rage, despair, most dramatically when he has not enough ego strength to fall back on. This ego strength seems to me the product of a benign secondary narcissism built on successful sublimations. It grows out of mastery of frustrations—

adversities that have been endured and transcended in creative conflict solutions; while ego weakness corresponds to a more or less malignant or negative secondary narcissism, which remains dependent on the pleasure-pain principle and the emotional reactions of escape from frustration by repression, distortion and denial.

The negative narcissism is at the core of neurotic and psychotic maladjustments. We find it in those human beings who give in to doubts whether they are able to cope with conflicts, or who have more or less given up faith altogether. They cannot stand the freedom of decisions, and, according to the all-or-none principle of pleasure and pain, they swing from narcissistic omnipotence illusions to illusions of impotence and despair. Constitutional endowment and the past and/or present hardships of fate contribute to the failures of narcissism. The original trust in life deteriorates into a more or less life-negating despair. Rainer Maria Rilke, an oversensitive poet often unable to deal with the frustrations of his existence, transcended his helplessness of negative narcissism in his poetry, which likely saved him from psychotic decompensation. He describes the disposition of malignant or negative narcissism [18]: "There are people flowering pale like white blossoms/ they die aghast of the cruel world/ and no one sees the horror stricken grimace/ to which the smiling of this tender race/ is distorted in nameless nights." *

In my practice, I see not a sharp division between benign and malignant narcissism, but a continuum from benign narcissism or ego strength, with flexible defenses against disorganizing anxieties,

---

* Rilke's "Das Stundenbuch Inselverlag" [18]:

> Da leben Menschen, weisserbluehte, blasse
> und sterben staunend an der schweren Welt
> und keiner sieht die klaffende Grimasse
> zu der das Laecheln einer zarten Rasse
> in namenlosen Naechten sich enstellt.
>
> Sie sind gegeben unter hundert Quaeler,
> und angeschrien von jeder Stunde Schlag,
> kreisen sie einsam um die Hospitaeler
> und warten angstoll auf den Einlasstag.
>
> *They are surrendered to hundreds of tormenters,*
> *Screamed at by every hour's bang*
> *They err lonely around the hospitals*
> *And wait anxiously for the day of admission.*

to a malignant narcissism or ego weakness, with the defenses against emergency increasingly breaking down.

A healthy narcissism holds the balance between self-esteem growing out of phase-adequate mastery of dangers, and dependency on auxiliary supplies of parental or other authoritative support. The child becomes increasingly conscious of reality, but what is this reality? Reality in psychoanalytic literature is sometimes understood as the world of science, a system of quantitatively measurable correlations. It is a great help for the growing child to acquire a high level of rational knowledge about the world that he has to live in. But according to Buytendijk,[5] one's world is no system of objective correlations; the scientific reality is a world without elements of quality, of color, sound, touch and taste, a world without meaning, a pure environment. This scientific reality is particularly a world without instincts and emotions. The world that the child learns to master is a world that is already evaluated by parents, teachers and peers, a conventionally accepted or criticized reality, full of emotional predilections and prejudices, from the scientific point of view full of erroneous, even incorrigible, ideas. The communist grows up in a reality that looks different from that of a Roman Catholic; the negro's immediate experience of reality is at variance with that of the white man. Insight into reality is conveyed to the child in the beginning by empathy or emotional participation. The child takes over the predilections and prejudices of his elders; he incorporates their standards and values in form of his ego ideal, their prohibitions in his superego. But in the transition from the pleasure-pain principle to the reality principle, the child experiences conflict. He has to make decisions, and decisions demand sacrifices. Is the constancy of interpersonal relations a higher value than the emotional escape from frustration by flight or fight? Parental punishments intensify the child's conflicts, the punishment of abandonment or withdrawal of love intensify his loneliness and helplessness, corporal punishment or castration threats endanger his bodily integrity. But an overprotected, overindulged child reared without setting of limits is also at a serious disadvantage in the development of a benign narcissism. The overprotected child reacts to real or imaginary dangers and frustrations that he has not learned to master step by step, with excessive anxieties, and he develops a mainly defensive narcissism. The overprotected child remains often dependent on narcissistic supplies with disorganized willfulness or discouraged will-lessness, without self-confidence in his own potentials.

Hartmann [11] has distinguished the ego from the self. The ego represents the level of organization that an individual has reached by synthesis of ego functions and the assimilation of a given reality, as well as by the differentiation from those external influences. The ego that has not reached the integration and mastery by sublimations adequate to its age level, whose emotions still automatically respond to pleasure and pain, is a weak ego, responsive but not responsible. The self is the sum of evaluations on which the ego bases its self-esteem in consensus with others or in rebellious dissension. This self-esteem approximates the objective state of ego development in a positive narcissism. The child loves himself not only when he feels loved by his family; in growing independence, he loves himself in spite of rejection by others. But such firmness of self-esteem is hard to reach, because of the power of human interdependence and solidarity. This solidarity is threatened by invidious comparisons, the injustice of fate that metes out unequal frustrations to the young and the old, the males and the females, the rich and the poor. Narcissism is beset by anxieties, doubts, self-consciousness, shame and guilt. A child may feel guilty not only when he displeases his parents, teachers and friends; even when he is better endowed and has richer opportunities, he feels exposed to the envy of his parents, his siblings or his peers. A self that he can love unambiguously is forever unreachable; the onward-and-upward thrust of his drives, erotic as well as aggressive, transcends the past and the present; the self is a project into the future. The peace and harmony of the original symbiosis remains a goal that can never be reached. It might be the ultimate goal of Freud's death instinct, but we never reach this goal consciously. We are embedded in the natural rhythm of life and death, waking and sleeping, activity and passivity, satisfaction and frustration. We know that it is dangerous for our survival to refuse the struggle with frustrations. A benign narcissism transcends the blows of frustration by changing the ego or changing the world, as far as possible, in the process of mutual adaptation, by autoplastic or alloplastic transformation. A complete refusal of transformation or transcendence causes death in life, even when a vegetating existence might continue. Thanatos tends to vanquish Eros in a psychosis, whether the ego functions are damaged by organic disease or whether ego development is arrested by evasion of conflicts. Ultimately, the world seems to be destroyed in a catastrophe that wipes out consciousness of a world and a self that have become inseparable. World destruction equals self-destruction in a psychosis. Rejected reality is distorted in hallucinations, illusions and delusions. Instead of realistic appraisal of the ego, the emotional self-assessment escapes into hypochondriac or self-condemning orgies of frustration rage, or this rage is compensatorily denied in phantasies of grandiosity and omnipotence that set up the false self of a more or less malignant narcissism that denies the defeat of the ego. But as long as there is life, there is hope. The Eros of benign narcissism can rise from defeat. In the repeated revival of original conflicts due to the repetition compulsion, the ego can correct its evasive indecisions and find new alternatives of conflict solution.

The original conflicts that infringe on the development of a benign narcissism arise in intimate interpersonal relations loaded with anxieties. For the sake of pleasing and winning the stronger other one, the weaker ego takes refuge in duplicity, hyprocrisy and pretended conformity. These defenses against interpersonal anxiety become an armor that hampers the spontaneous ego development. The weaker the ego, the greater is the need to be loved, since nothing can so strongly confirm self-confidence as to be loved by another human being. But to be loved is different from the courage of active love, which takes the risk of surrender to the other whom he trusts. In his essay on narcissism, Freud suggests that the ego is weakened by love; the love object is idealized, overevaluated, but the ego is supposed to be impoverished, humbled, in the case of unrequited love even humiliated. This passively receiving love is frequently used as a defense against anxiety.

Narcissistic libido does not necessarily impoverish the ego. It is true that there are conflicts between object love and narcissism, between self-preservation and altruism, Sartre's pour-soi and pour-autrui, the striving to become one's own ideal and the ideal of the beloved. An intimate relation of parent and child, lover and beloved can, under the pressure of anxiety or rage, deteriorate into a master-slave relation. It is true that the commitment to active love implies a risk, the beloved is losable, but a love that transcends anxieties enriches both lovers even in the face of frustrations. Shakespeare seems to have expressed the true state of active love very well when he has Juliet say (Romeo and Juliet, 2:2):

My bounty is as boundless as the sea,
My love as deep; the more I give to thee,
The more I have, for both are infinite.

This same paradoxical truth is expressed by St. Matthew (16:25):

For whosoever will save his life shall lose it:
and whosoever will lose his life for my sake shall find it.

The anxious defensive narcissism holds on to life, but the lover is generous through the power of Eros transcending Thanatos. Even in the ultimate loss of life, Eros triumphs in the survivor by the preservation of loving memories; it mitigates the abandoned person's depression. The bereaved partner transcends the blow of destiny to his narcissism. Love transforms depression into grief that accepts inevitable frustration through the labor of mourning.

In the parent-child relation, there is such a discrepancy between the parents' strength, knowledge and competence in comparison to the child's helpless dependency that there is the danger that the loving care of the parent, particularly of the mother, might deteriorate into a sadomasochistic relation of dominance or possession. The mother may exploit or appropriate the child, or she may make herself a slave to the child's whims and wishes. This inequality, which is misused by parental defensive narcissism in a master-slave relation, also creeps into adolescent or adult erotic relations where the narcissistic demands of one or both partners may infringe on their capacity for spontaneous mutuality. The inequality between male and female is a source of latent conflict. Freud thought that the Oedipus conflict is solved by the male's giving up the claim for exclusive possession of the mother for the narcissistic gain of preserving his penis. The girl may give up her narcissistic claims, because she has already been punished by castration, or will be further damaged in her narcissism by cruel penetration. Castration anxiety and penis envy seem to me to be symbolic expressions of a male-female conflict that demands or offers narcissistic sacrifices in order to repress anxieties in the interpersonal relation. Genuine sacrifices must be made and are made by men as well as by women for the sake of the constancy of their mutual relation and their relation to their children. These sacrifices imply the endurance of inevitable frustrations, but they cannot be enforced by threat or punishment. When enforced, these sacrifices deteriorate into sadomasochistic manipulation, into revenge for the frustration rage that makes the other responsible for the hardships of fate, or into surrender to the partner for the sake of exploitation in an unending claw and tooth struggle for supremacy of the defensive narcissism of either partner. Many parent-child relations and husband-wife relations collapse at this impasse if the anxiety-laden conflict between the I and the You has been covered over by foul compromises and has not been faced squarely. The woman, who expects that the husband has to sacrifice his own freedom of development for her narcissistic need to be adored and protected, misses the grace of mutuality as much as the husband, who takes her gifts and services for granted as a tribute to his defensive narcissism. The sexual enjoyment can be a bond of spontaneous mutuality that enriches the benign narcissism of both partners, but the sexual act can also be degraded to a dutiful performance or a form of exploitation that leaves the total personalities empty, bored and unfulfilled, if there is no process of mutual inspiration going on which furthers a transcending development into the future of both. Likewise, the relation of parent and child that does not increase the potentialites of development in both does not contribute to the happiness of either.

Psychoanalysis has to demask the various self-deceptions and illusions that arise in the pursuit of happiness by emotional alarm signals. Many persons pretend to be happy even if they are not; others complain about unhappiness with the indignant accusations of a typical "injustice collector." Happiness cannot be enforced, it is a gift of grace. A tension will always exist between the present state of development and its aspired transcendance into the future. There is anxiety in all decisions. The yearning for unlimited narcissistic omnipotence that would gratify autistic as well as symbiotic wishes can never be fulfilled. Sacrifices of narcissistic wishes are necessary to transcend inevitable frustrations. Limitations arouse anxieties, which enhance a defensive narcissism that tries to deny the tension and discrepancy between ego and self-image. Man sometimes believes that he is already what he wants to become; conceit, arrogance, boasting and bragging mask the anxieties of indecision and incompletion. Sartre[19] has expressed this discrepancy in a paradoxical form: Man is not what he is and he is what he is not. In less parodoxical terms this means that man is in a constant flux of becoming. In this process he lets go what he has achieved and received, not to be deprived and to descend to Sartre's nothingness and meaninglessness, but to rise to a higher synthesis of his potentialities. Thus, narcissism cannot settle down in a complacent identity of ego and self. Self-deception, according to Sartre, stems from bad faith. It leads to repressions, dissociations, denial and other forms of distorting defenses. But it is not the unconscious, anarchic cauldron of instincts that Sartre makes responsible for these defensive distortions. In order to repress, deny or distort, impulses that are unacceptable to oneself or others must pass a censorship, if only fleetingly, in order to be discarded or repressed in view of the danger signal of anxiety. Emotional signals are deceptive because they represent magical solutions of conflicts where frustrations have to be endured and transcended in hard labor. Protesting rage reactions try to remove the source of discomfort by a short circuiting gesture of elimination or destruction. Egocentric search of pleasure and comfort demands immediate gratification, envy tries to even the score by hook and by crook, vengeful impulses insist on nothing less than a complete defeat of the opponent and his unconditional surrender. Emotions remain tied to the pleasure-pain principle to avoid the pain of conflict, but the rationalist who denies the power of emotions remains under their sway the more he shuts his eyes to them and relies on his rationalizations. Emotions remain self-centered, if a defensive narcissism persists and the individual cannot sacrifice part of his self-interest for the sake of the communion with others. The conflict of I and you may lead to tragic guilt when the Oedipus conflict remains unresolved.

The guilt of the Oedipus tragedy stemmed from the parents' anxiety elicited by the oracle that foretold the murder and superseding of the father by the son. Narcissistic anxiety drove the parents of Oedipus to abandon the child, leaving him to a cruel fate of almost certain death. By the complexities of fate, the guilt of the parents is transferred to the descendents. Basically, every parent is destined to be superseded by his descendants. Not only the child's but also the parents' narcissism rebels against destiny. The incestuous motive expresses the persistent regression to parent-child symbiosis; it stifles the process of growing individuation, and it destroys the family solidarity by the murderous impulses of egocentric competition. The classic tragedies of Oedipus and Hamlet demonstrate the conflict between individual self-preservation and family solidarity. Even a guilt that was removed from the hero's intention (Oedipus), the mother's breach of fidelity and the fratricidal murder of the father—in the case of Hamlet—this all-too human guilt is transferred to the son as a challenge. A sense of guilt that stems from the binding solidarity of men arouses indignation, and it demands from the heir of injustice a decision to be or not to be, a sacrifice, in the case of Oedipus and Hamlet, the acceptance of a tragic destiny.

Sacrifice has frequently been degraded as a form of neurotic masochism in psychoanalytic literature. The very survival of mankind depends on our basic solidarity, which is actualized in the animal by automatic instinct regulation. In man, this solidarity is actualized instinctively in the mother-child symbiosis. But the actualization of solidarity in later life is frequently squelched by prevailing narcissistic interests of the isolated and alienated individual who spends his energies in the conflicts between self-preservation and solidarity, and in failures of defense against the hardships of fate. The Oedipus conflict is of such crucial importance in the development of man because narcissistic self-interest and solidarity come to a clash and demand decisions. Each child inherits his parents' guilt—Freud [10] spoke of borrowed guilt feelings; he inherits their neurotic maladaptations, their disharmonies and human incompletions. The Christians believed in inherited sin and have never been really comforted by the promise of salvation. The Oedipus conflict is a challenge to the child to find a solution for the problem, not only on a rational level of enlightened self-interest, but on the emotional level of a benign narcissism and human solidarity. Man in his existential anxiety has to make conscious decisions between being and nothingness, between his responsibilty for personal self-preservation and his loyalty to family and larger units of solidarity. His longing for the peace and harmony of primary narcissism or primary love was in earlier periods of human history gratified by religious experience of unity with God, oceanic harmony, although this peace with God frequently became a sentimental illusion, or was torn up by fanatical persecution of those who did not share the faith. The intellectual of Western culture has, at present, no universal faith that provides security, and human solidarity is still a utopia. Man acts in bad faith when his defensive narcissism in an emotional conflict represses, denies or dissociates his existential anxiety, the danger signal of frustration. He cannot endure the tension between his longing for mastery of fate and divine perfection, on the one hand, and his recognition of his tragic inability to reach this superhuman goal, on the other hand.

Existential philosophy, as well as psychoanalysis, has taken up the cudgels for the individual in his struggle for authenticity, i.e., truth to himself and genuine spontaneity, holding that both are in danger of being lost under the pressure of a mass society whose rational means of technology are far ahead of emotional control. Education is too much directed toward accumulation of technology, facts, and data. This knowledge, though useful, does not provide the means of emotional control. Psychoanalysis has to stress the responsibility of the individual to revise evasive decisions that have led to lopsided defensive habits. Psychoanalysis cannot abolish tragic sacrifices in the course of responsible decisions. The patient feels frequently irresponsibly determined by the forces of unconscious instincts. When the narcissistic defenses fail, the individual feels doomed to isolation, alienation, disharmony in his intimate relations. Psychoanalysis accepts the challenge to reawaken the original good faith of the individual by leading him back to the original emotional conflicts in the living experience of transference and countertransference. The emotional conflict between self-preservation and preservation of human solidarity cannot be solved once and for all, but in the encounters of I and You that transcend the split between them, the frustration rage can come into the open and gradually subside. In the psychoanalytic encounter, the patient can learn to forgive himself and his parents, to sacrifice his claim for unconditional love, his grandiose protest against destiny and his enraged craving for magical help; he can give up the masochistic submission to authority for the sake of rewards; and he can outgrow the negative therapeutic reaction of revenge. In psychoanalytic treatment, the genuine I-You relations are gradually crystallized out of the distortions of transference-countertransference maneuvers that are dictated by the narcissistic defenses against emergency emotions of anxiety, rage, hatred, envy and revenge. Neurotic anxieties and psychotic panic are differentiated from deeper existential anxieties, neurotic guilt feelings from existential responsibility. The analyst cannot abolish existential anxiety and guilt, but he can bring repressed conflicts to awareness and strengthen the sense of responsibility. The genuine sacrifice of the distorted goals of a defensive narcissism makes room for a higher level of integration of egosyntonic goals. In the transition from the unconscious innocence of primary autonomy to a preconsciously and consciously controlled benign narcissism, the erotic forces of spontaneous generosity are freed for a new beginning, a new balance between the authenticity of a benign narcissism and a trusting mutuality in interpersonal relations.

REFERENCES

1. Abraham, K.: Selected Papers. The First Pregenital Stage of the Libido, New York, Basic, 1953, pp. 248-279.
2. Balint, M.: Primary Love and Psychoanalytic Technique, London, Hogarth Press, 1952.
3. Bibring, E.: Das Problem der Depression (The Problem of Depression), Psyche (Stuttgart) 6:82-101, 1952.
4. Bing, J., McLaughlin, F., and Marburg, R.: The Metapsychology of Narcissism; The Study of the Child, vol. 14, New York, Internat Univ Press, 1959.
5. Buytendijk, F. J. J.: Allgemeine Theorie der menschlichen Haltung und Bewegung, Berlin, Göttingen u. Heidelberg, Springer, 1956.
6. Erikson, E. H.: Childhood and Society, New York, Norton, 1950.
7. Freud, A.: The Ego and the Mechanisms of Defense, New York, Internat Univ Press, 1948.
8. Freud, S.: On Narcissism: An Introduction, Collected Papers IV, London, Hogarth Press, 1952.
9. ———: Beyond the Pleasure Principle, London, Hogarth Press, 1948.
10. ———: The Ego and the Id, London, Hogarth Press, 1929.
11. Hartmann, H.: Essays of Ego Psychology, New York, Internat Univ Press, 1964.
12. Hegel, G. W. F.: The Phenomenology of Mind, trans. by Baillie, J. B., New York, Macmillan, 1947.
13. Hendrick, I.: Instinct and the Ego During Infancy, Psa Quart 11:33-58, 1942.
14. Klein, M.: Contributions to Psychoanalysis, London, Hogarth Press, 1946.
15. Mahler, M.: On Child Psychosis and Schizophrenia. Autistic and Symbiotic Infantile Psychosis, Psychoanal Stud Child 7:265-305, 1952.
16. Rado, S., and Daniels, E. G.: Changing Concepts of Psychoanalytic Medicine, New York, Grune, 1956.
17. Rapaport, D.: The Autonomy of the Ego, Bull Menninger Clin 15:113-123, 1951.
18. Rilke, R. M.: Das Stundenbuch Inselverlag, Leipzig, 1918, pp. 85-86.
19. Sartre, J. P.: L'être et le Néant, Paris, Librairie Gallimard, 1948.
20. Schachtel, E. S.: Metamorphosis, New York, Basic, 1957.
21. White, R. W.: The Abnormal Personality, New York, Ronald Press, 1947.

Discussion

Rudolf Marburg, MD

Private Practice of Psychoanalysis, Baltimore

Dr. weigert's definition of malignant narcissism as equated with destructive aggression, if I understand her correctly, puzzles me somewhat. The use of the word *narcissism* often is accompanied by an attitude of derogation almost as if it were a bad name. In my mind, narcissism is an important constructive aspect of the individual's personality. It is troublesome and a serious and far-reaching problem only when we deal with narcissism of extensive proportions (or, as I would rather think of it, as pathologic narcissism instead of malignant).

My understanding of some aspects of this whole difficult concept of narcissism is this. Primary narcissism I see as the libidinal investment of the organism prior to the establishment of more differentiated psychic structures. Secondary narcissism I see as the libidinal investment in the various parts and functions of psychic structures as they progressively develop, the self-image and the ego ideal. The infant originally is thought to repudiate all that is tension-producing or causes pain as alien and not belonging to itself, and to see all that is gratifying as part of itself.

It seems to me that one could understand the behavior of the infant in Dr. Weigert's chapter, who refused to take food from the tense adult, as a turning away from the pain-producing source, a form of flight reaction—later denial, repression or avoidance as the ego emerges as a functioning structure. We see in our daily practice how patients operate often on the "What I don't see does not exist" principle. It appears to me that overstimulation is the main culprit that interferes with the maturation process and prevents the proper development of various ego functions as well as with the process of neutralization. Neutralized energy is essential for the modification of instinctual aims as well as for further maturation of ego functions. Early narcissistic investment untempered by reality considerations, and primitive identifications, like the omnipotent parent figures, also unmodified by reality testing and as yet undifferentiated from the self-representations, are held

239

onto or regressed to, under the onslaught of overstimulated libidinal and aggressive drives, in order to cope with the intolerable
tension of helplessness against external as well as internal dangers.

Such onslaughts on the still underdeveloped ego interfere with
the normal progress of development of stable ego functions and
identifications. This, in turn, leaves the ego more vulnerable; aggressive, destructive, impulses cannot be harnessed by the poorly
equipped ego because of their unmodified nature and strength.
They are aroused easily due to the inability to adapt the archaic
ego ideal, as well as the primitive self-image, to more objective and
reality-oriented proportions. Giving up this omnipotent position
provokes tensions and exposes the patient to danger. The greater
the investment in early archaic self-representation, the more
pathologic the narcissism.

In our work with patients, we are constantly confronted with a
greater or lesser degree of such narcissistic investments, which
permeate the entire functioning of the individual. It takes part in
the maintenance of symptoms and attitudes, and unless the patient
can give up or moderate this narcissistic investment in the symptom and is able to tolerate the pain of relinquishing his omnipotence, he cannot abandon the symptom. The shift of narcissistic
investment from archaic self-image and primitive ego functions to
more and more reality-oriented and sublimated ego functions and
aims is an important and healthy course of development. Equally
essential is the transformation of primitive narcissistic investment
into idealization of important introjects, like the superego and the
ego ideal. This latter form of narcissism supplies the power and
impetus toward higher and more stable development of the ego.

In treatment, it is important to help the patient use his narcissism for further maturation. Often the therapist is inclined to
protect the patient's primitive narcissism because of the pain it
causes the patient when he has to relinquish it. We are not serving
the patient well if we allow this to happen, rather than helping
him to bear the pain by sympathetic understanding.

DR. WEIGERT

I am really in full agreement with Dr. Marburg. I am also will-
ing to change *malignant* into *pathologic*. I do not quite give up
anxiety because *pain* and *anxiety* belong together. I would think
anxiety is more a kind of indecision of what to do with a pain,
running away or having some kind of narcissistic defense.

APPENDIX c *is a continuation of Dr. Kubie's Chapter 9,* The Future of the Private Hospital. *Copy for it arrived after* Crosscurrents in Psychiatry *&* Psychoanalysis *was in pages.*

APPENDIX C

RELATION OF PRIVATE PSYCHIATRIC HOSPITAL TO ADOLESCENT PATIENTS

THAT ADOLESCENTS MAKE UP an increasing proportion of hospital patients is challenging our hospitals with new problems and demands for the solution of which the private psychiatric hospital is essential. There are arguments for creating within the general structure of the hospital a separate division for these younger patients, with its own residential setup, activities, educational facilities, supervisory personnel, self-governing organization and monetary system.

In support of this, it is pointed out that the problems of this age-group are so interwoven with their compulsive rebellion against the adult world that to place the adult and the adolescent together at the start of treatment automatically transplants their antiadult patterns into the hospital before it has had an opportunity to exercise any mitigating influence. Moreover, some feel that the younger group requires a two-stage operation: first in its own world, then moving during a second phase of hospital treatment into a world that includes adults. Others object that a separate milieu for the adolescents intensifies their ganging impulses, thus creating almost insoluble problems for any hospital trying to be liberal in dealing with rebellious patients, out of its recognition that such rebelliousness can often be a step towards health. No one can pretend to have the only way to solve these problems. All we know is that to confront the younger patient with the traditional hospital structure gives little possibility of helping him.

This age-group creates still another set of problems because of the necessarily long duration of treatment. Some measure of emotional retardation is central to many psychiatric illnesses among adults; but it is most strikingly true for the younger group. The solution of adolescent disturbances requires, among other things, that adolescents be given time to mature emotionally. This takes time enough for them to relive the maturational process in a corrective fashion, to make progress and to regress over and over

241

again. This is essential for any relearning process, and such time has to be measured in years rather than months. Yet few adolescents are sick enough to be legally committable. Therefore, after the ages of 18 to 21 (this varies in different states) few of them can be held in hospitals against their wills without legal action (i.e. merely at the request of parents or guardians), even if this is desirable, which is another matter long debated but never settled. Consequently, a program of treatment begun in midadolescence might continue into the years when they could no longer be held against their wills. No public institution will hold them long enough.

One further consideration. The entire hospital invests an enormous amount of effort, hope, affection, and emotional dedication to these young people; and everyone suffers pain and some anger at each setback, especially because the regressive behavior of one may infect others and lead to group outbreaks of similar misbehavior. Therefore, each relapse arouses an impulse to crack down and even to rupture the patient's relationship to the hospital and to the therapist by dismissing him. Often one is tempted to rationalize this step with the damning judgment that the patient is not treatable, that he cannot make use of therapeutic opportunities, that he cannot be reached and, of course, that he is schizophrenic. Yet this solves no problems, just as schools never solve a child's problems by flunking him out. To resist these natural impulses requires of the hospital and its whole staff (administration, doctors, psychologists, nurses, aides) great maturity, strength, patience, and a willingness to keep on trying in the face even of painful criticism—while the patient's family is becoming understandably short of patience. Obviously, any attempt to meet the problems of this age is a challenge difficult for our hospitals to accept. Here, especially, we need the private psychiatric hospital to show the way.

Participants

Dates denote years at The Sheppard and Enoch Pratt Hospital

MARVIN L. ADLAND, MD
1944–1946
Private Practice of Psychoanalysis,
Washington

A. RUSSELL ANDERSON, MD
1935–1939
Private Practice of Psychoanalysis,
Baltimore; Secretary, American
Psychoanalytic Association,
1963–1964

LEO H. BARTEMEIER, MD
Medical Director, The Seton
Psychiatric Institute, Baltimore

EUGENE B. BRODY, MD
Professor and Chairman, Depart-
ment of Psychiatry, Director, The
Psychiatric Institute, University
of Maryland School of Medicine,
Baltimore

JOSEPH O. CHASSELL, PHD, MD
1931–1938
Senior Psychiatrist, Austen Riggs
Center, Incorporated, Stockbridge,
Massachusetts; Past President,
Western New England Psycho-
analytic Association

ROBERT A. CLARK, MD
Director, Northeast Mental Health
Clinic, Philadelphia

MABEL B. COHEN, MD
1938–1942
Private Practice of Psychoanalysis,
Chevy Chase, Maryland

ROBERT A. COHEN, MD
1938–1941
Director, Clinical Investigations,
National Institute of Mental
Health, Bethesda

WILLIAM T. DIXON, MD
1965–
Senior Psychiatrist, The Sheppard
and Enoch Pratt Hospital, Towson

LEON EISENBERG, MD
1950–1952
Professor of Child Psychiatry,
The Johns Hopkins University
School of Medicine, Baltimore;
Editor, American Journal of
Orthopsychiatry

JOEL ELKES, MD
Henry Phipps Professor of Psychia-
try and Director, Department of
Psychiatry and Behavioral Sciences,
The Johns Hopkins University,
Psychiatrist-in-Chief, The Johns
Hopkins Hospital, Baltimore

BLISS FORBUSH, LL D
1959–
President, Board of Trustees,
The Sheppard and Enoch Pratt
Hospital, Towson; Headmaster
Emeritus, The Friends School,
Baltimore

ROBERT W. GIBSON, MD
1960–
Medical Director, The Sheppard

243

and Enoch Pratt Hospital

IVES HENDRICK, MD
1927–1928

Director of Clinical Psychiatry, Massachusetts Mental Health Center; Clinical Professor of Psychiatry Emeritus, Harvard Medical School, Boston; President, American Psychoanalytic Association, 1953–1955

LAWRENCE S. KUBIE, MD
1959–

Consultant, Research and Training, The Sheppard and Enoch Pratt Hospital, Towson; Visiting Professor of Psychiatry, Jefferson Medical College, Philadelphia; Clinical Professor of Psychiatry, University of Maryland School of Medicine, Baltimore

RUDOLF MARBURG, MD
1940–1945

Private Practice of Psychoanalysis, Baltimore

ALEXANDER REID MARTIN, MD, DPM   *1927–1934*

Honorary Member of the Staff of The Sheppard and Enoch Pratt Hospital, Towson; Life Fellow, American Psychiatric Association

FRANCIS McLAUGHLIN, MD
1940–1947

Private Practice of Psychoanalysis, Baltimore; Director, The Baltimore Psychoanalytic Institute, 1953–1959

RUSSELL R. MONROE, MD

Professor of Psychiatry, Director of Graduate Training, The Psychiatric Institute, University of Maryland School of Medicine, Baltimore

GARY O. MORRIS, MD

Private Practice of Psychiatry, Washington

HARRY M. MURDOCK, MD
1930–

Consultant to the Board of Trustees, The Sheppard and Enoch Pratt Hospital, Towson; Medical Director, 1949–1963

DOUGLAS NOBLE, MD
1930–1939

Clinical Professor of Psychiatry, George Washington University School of Medicine; Private Practice of Psychoanalysis, Washington

SAMUEL NOVEY, MD
1940–1942, 1944–1948, 1966–

Director of Training, The Sheppard and Enoch Pratt Hospital, Towson; Associate Professor of Psychiatry, The Johns Hopkins University School of Medicine; Private Practice of Psychoanalysis, Baltimore

KENT E. ROBINSON, MD
1964–

Director of Outpatient Services, The Sheppard and Enoch Pratt Hospital, Towson

SEYMOUR J. ROSENBERG, MD

Clinical Professor of Psychiatry, Georgetown University School of Medicine; Private Practice of Psychoanalysis, Washington

CLARENCE G. SCHULZ, MD
1963–

Director of Inpatient Services, The Sheppard and Enoch Pratt Hospital, Towson

HAROLD F. SEARLES, MD
1963–

Supervising and Training Analyst, The Washington Psychoanalytic Institute; Clinical Professor of Psychiatry, Georgetown University School of Medicine, Washington; Consultant in Psychotherapy,

The Sheppard and Enoch Pratt Hospital, Towson

G. WILSON SHAFFER, PhD
1928–
Professor of Psychology and Dean of the Faculty, The Johns Hopkins University, Baltimore; Consultant in Psychology, The Sheppard and Enoch Pratt Hospital, Towson

FREDERICK SNYDER, MD
Chief, Section on Psychophysiology of Sleep, Adult Psychiatry Branch, National Institute of Mental Health, Bethesda

SARAH S. TOWER, MD
Private Practice of Psychiatry and Psychoanalysis; Associate Professor of Psychiatry, The Johns Hopkins

University School of Medicine, Baltimore

PHILIP S. WAGNER, MD
1938–1941
Medical Director, Mental Health Development Center (Subsidiary of Retail Clerks Local 770 and Food Employers Benefit Fund), Los Angeles; Past President, Institute for Psychoanalytic Medicine of Southern California, *1959–1960*

EDITH V. WEIGERT, MD
1938–1940
Private Practice of Psychoanalysis, Chevy Chase, Maryland; Chairman of the Faculty, Washington School of Psychiatry, *1961–*

Index of Subjects

Index of Names

257